"Youth is a beautiful dream, on whose brightness books shed a blinding dust. Will ever the day come when the wise link the joy of knowledge to youth's dream? Will ever the day come when Nature becomes the teacher of man, humanity his book and life his school? Youth's joyous purpose cannot be fulfilled until that day comes. Too slow is our march toward spiritual elevation, because we make so little use of youth's ardor."

KAHLIL GIBRAN

The beloved visionary whose profound wisdom and inspirational writings have stirred the hearts of millions, pictures here a joyous world free of suffering, a world of enlightenment unflawed by ignorance, a world whose great minds reject superstition, a world of progress that abhors corruption.

ABOUT THE AUTHOR

KAHLIL GIBRAN was born in Bechari, Lebanon, in 1883. His early literary work comprised prose poems in Arabic. His plays were known to the entire Arabic world from China to Spain and gave rise to a new word, "Gibranism." He is remembered as one of the most read and respected authors of the twentieth century by both eastern and western cultures alike. Gibran died in 1931 at Saint Vincent's Hospital in New York's Greenwich Village. His *Voice of the Master* and *The Broken Wings* are also available in Bantam paperback editions.

KAHLIL GIBRAN

THOUGHTS AND MEDITATIONS

*Translated from the Arabic and
edited by Anthony R. Ferris*

*This low-priced Bantam Book
has been completely reset in a type face
designed for easy reading, and was printed
from new plates. It contains the complete
text of the original hard-cover edition.*
NOT ONE WORD HAS BEEN OMITTED.

THOUGHTS AND MEDITATIONS

*A Bantam Book / published by arrangement with
The Citadel Press, Inc.*

PRINTING HISTORY

Citadel edition published October 1960

Book Sales Inc. edition published May 1967
2nd printing......April 1968

Bantam edition published December 1968

2nd printing

3rd printing

4th printing

5th printing

6th printing

7th printing

Published simultaneously in the United States and Canada

*Bantam Books are published by Bantam Books, Inc., a subsidiary
of Grosset & Dunlap, Inc. Its trade-mark, consisting of the words
"Bantam Books" and the portrayal of a bantam, is registered in the
United States Patent Office and in other countries. Marca Registrada.
Bantam Books, Inc., 271 Madison Avenue, New York, N.Y. 10016*

PRINTED IN THE UNITED STATES OF AMERICA

Contents

✿

Preface

❧

In his youth, the author of *The Prophet* conceived the universe as perfect and devoid of evil. He pictured a joyous world free of suffering, a world of enlightenment unflawed by ignorance, a world whose great minds rejected superstitions, a world of progress that abhorred corruption. Justice and wisdom lived side by side in this paradise of his conception, and unity and good will prevailed among men. But after finding out that the haven he fashioned was different from mundane reality, he felt disappointed and embittered.

Gibran had looked upon the heads of state and the hierarchs of the religions as truly the pillars of society. He expected them to provide examples of justice and wisdom. He assumed that the privileges and the plenty they enjoyed were their due for the noble services they rendered to their people. He imagined that it was on this account that the people yielded them honor, trust, and obedience. They would not have obtained these, he assumed, were they not worthy.

It was in this light that he looked upon the rulers

and their luxurious life and failed to see how they exploited the people. When he began to perceive the realities of life, he saw the rich abusing the poor who lived under the yoke of slavery and despotism. That which Gibran called "tyranny" masked itself under the name of "politics." And the prophet from Lebanon began to express his feelings through scorching articles in Arabic newspapers, books, and magazines. I have included a selection of these in the present volume.

The world that Gibran was seeking was a world of understanding, a world of logic, and of positive thinking. The people of such a world are not beguiled by impostors and do not cling to superstitions. For them the mind is the only lamp that illuminates the dark path of ignorance, and this lamp should be kept eternally lit.

Gibran's life was an example of the belief in the authority of the great mind. His keen mind led him to open a new road for himself. The world that Gibran imagined is a place illumined by reason and understanding. In it superstitions and fantasies melt like ice under the rays of the sun. But alas, what is in the actual world we live in? Every kind of ruler has won power except the ruler with a mind. The honest man is forced into deceit, the impostor holds sway, and the people are chained by custom and tradition. Their religion bows to hardened custom. The people live in the ruts trodden by their ancestors; they do not follow the light of their own minds or the dictates of their own hearts. This has led the people into narrow, separated faiths and suspicious, unfriendly, separated nations, instead of a universal faith and a world nation. Thus they remained the victims of superstitions. And in the world so conditioned, success is gained by the sacrifice of conscience and honor. The man of integrity sinks into the jaws of poverty. The honest man is reviled and the liar admired and rewarded with possessions.

Gibran lamented such a world. His sorrowing songs became a beautiful and soothing melody. In his poetry, this beloved son of Lebanon projected a bewildered person, a convert, a skeptic, or a believer according to the vicissitudes in his inner self. This diversity reflects the wealth and philosophic depths of his knowledge, expressed in both his Arabic and English writings.

Gibran came to this world to say his word and to benefit his fellow men. It is my sincerest hope that *Thoughts and Meditations*, the words of wisdom which the Prophet of Lebanon wrote and uttered, will foster love and peace, and enlarge understanding throughout the world.

ANTHONY R. FERRIS

The Poet from Baalbek

❦

Sarkis Effandi, one of Gibran's closest friends, was highly regarded among the intelligentsia of Lebanon. He owned a publishing house and a daily Arabic newspaper called Lisan-Ul-Hal. In the year 1912, the Arab League of Progress, organized for the promotion of Arab unity and culture, decided to honor the great Lebanese poet Khalil Effandi Mutran.

Since Sarkis was the head of the committee honoring the poet, he extended an invitation to his friend Gibran, now settled in New York, to join them in Beirut on that occasion. Gibran could not make the trip, but he sent Sarkis a story with instructions to read it in his behalf before the poet. In the story, which eulogises the poet, Gibran expresses his belief in the transmigration of souls and praises the great soul reincarnated in the honored poet.

IN THE CITY OF BAALBEK, THE YEAR 112 B.C.

The Emir sat on his golden throne surrounded by glittering lamps and gilded censers. The aromatic scent of

1

the latter filled the palace. At his right and left sides were the high priests and the chiefs; the slaves and guards stood immobile before him like statues of bronze erected before the face of the sun.

After the cantors had chanted echoing hymns, an elderly vizier stood before the Emir, and in a voice modulated in the serenity of age, said, "Oh great and merciful Prince, yesterday there arrived in our city a sage from India who believes in a diversity of religions and speaks of strange things difficult to understand. He preaches the doctrine of the transmigration of souls and the incarnation of spirits which move from one generation to another seeking more and more perfect avatars until they become godlike. This sage seeks an audience with you to explain his dogma."

The Emir shook his head, smiled, and said, "From India come many strange and wonderful things. Call in the sage that we may hear his words of wisdom."

As soon as he uttered these words, a dark-hued, aged man walked in with dignity and stood before the Emir. His large brown eyes spoke, without words, of deep secrets. He bowed, raised his head, his eyes glittered, and he commenced to speak.

He explained how the spirits pass from one body to another, elevated by the good acts of the medium which they choose, and influenced by their experience in each existence; aspiring toward a splendor that exalts them and strengthens their growth by Love that makes them both happy and miserable. . . .

Then the philosopher dwelt on the manner in which the spirits move from place to place in their quest for perfection, atoning in the present for sins committed in the past, and reaping in one existence what they had sown in another.

Observing signs of restlessness and weariness on the Emir's countenance, the old vizier whispered to the sage, "You have preached enough at present; please postpone the rest of your discourse until our next meeting."

Thereupon the sage withdrew from the Emir's presence and sat among the priests and chiefs, closing his eyes as if weary of gazing into the deeps of Existence.

After a profound silence, similar to the trance of a prophet, the Emir looked to the right and to the left and inquired, "Where is our poet, we have not seen him for many days. What became of him? He always attended our meeting."

A priest responded, saying, "A week ago I saw him sitting in the portico of Ishtar's temple, staring with glazed and sorrowful eyes at the distant evening twilight as if one of his poems had strayed among the clouds."

And a chief added, "I saw him yesterday standing beneath the shade of the willow and cypress trees. I greeted him but he gave no heed to my greeting, and remained submerged in the deep sea of his thoughts and meditations."

Then the Grand Eunuch said, "I saw him today in

the palace garden, with pale and haggard face, sighing, and his eyes full of tears."

"Go seek out this unhappy soul, for his absence from our midst troubles us," ordered the Emir.

At this command, the slaves and the guards left the hall to seek the poet, while the Emir and his priests and chiefs remained in the assembly hall awaiting their return. It seemed as if their spirits had felt his invisible presence among them.

Soon the Grand Eunuch returned and prostrated himself at the feet of the Emir like a bird shot by the arrow of an archer. Whereupon the Emir shouted at him saying, "What happened . . . what have you to say?" The slave raised his head and said in a trembling voice, "We found the poet dead in the palace garden."

Then the Emir rose and hastened sorrowfully to the palace garden, preceded by his torchbearers and followed by the priests and the chiefs. At the end of the garden close by the almond and pomegranate trees, the yellow light of the torches brought the dead youth into their sight. His corpse lay upon the green grass like a withered rose.

"Look how he embraced his viol as if the two were lovers pledged to die together!" said one of the Emir's aides.

Another one said, "He still stares, as in life, at the heart of space; he still seems to be watching the invisible movements of an unknown god among the planets."

And the high priest addressed the Emir, saying, "Tomorrow let us bury him, as a great poet, in the shade of Ishtar's temple, and let the townspeople march in his funeral procession, while youths sing his poems and virgins strew flowers over his sepulchre. Let it be a commemoration worthy of his genius."

The Emir nodded his head without diverting his eyes from the young poet's face, pale with the veil of Death. "We have neglected this pure soul when he was alive, filling the Universe with the fruit of his brilliant intellect and spreading throughout space the aromatic scent of his soul. If we do not honor him now, we will be mocked and reviled by the gods and the nymphs of the prairies and valleys.

"Bury him in this spot where he breathed his last and let his viol remain between his arms. If you wish to honor him and pay him tribute, tell your children that the Emir had neglected him and was the cause of his miserable and lonely death." Then the monarch asked, "Where is the sage from India?" And the sage walked forth and said, "Here, oh great Prince."

And the Emir inquired, saying, "Tell us, oh sage, will the gods ever restore me to this world as a prince and bring back the deceased poet to life? Will my spirit become incarnated in a body of a great king's son, and will the poet's soul transmigrate into the body of another genius? Will the sacred Law make him stand before the face of Eternity that he may compose poems of Life? Will he be restored that I may honor him and pay him tribute by showering upon him precious gifts and rewards that will enliven his heart and inspire his soul?"

And the sage answered the Emir, saying, *"Whatever the soul longs for, will be attained by the spirit. Remember, oh great Prince, that the sacred Law which restores the sublimity of Spring after the passing of Winter will reinstate you a prince and him a genius poet."*

The Emir's hopes were revived and signs of joy appeared on his face. He walked toward his palace thinking and meditating upon the words of the sage: *"Whatever the soul longs for, will be attained by the spirit."*

IN CAIRO, EGYPT, THE YEAR 1912 A.D.

The full moon appeared and spread her silver garment upon the city. The Prince of the land stood at the balcony of his palace gazing at the clear sky and pondering upon the ages that have passed along the bank of the Nile. He seemed to be reviewing the processions of the nations that marched, together with Time, from the Pyramid to the palace of Abedine.

As the circle of the Prince's thoughts widened and extended into the domain of his dreams, he looked at his boon companion sitting by his side and said, "My soul is thirsty; recite a poem for me tonight."

And the boon companion bowed his head and began a pre-Islamic poem. But before he had recited many stanzas, the Prince interrupted him saying, "Let us hear a modern poem . . . a more recent one."

And, bowing, the boon companion began to recite verses composed by a Hadramout poet. The Prince stopped him again, saying, "More recent . . . a more recent poem."

The singer raised his hand and touched his forehead as if trying to recall to memory all the poems composed by contemporary poets. Then his eyes glittered, his face brightened, and he began to sing lovely verses in soothing rhythm, full of enchantment.

Intoxicated and seeming to feel the movement of hidden hands beckoning him from his palace to a distant land, the Prince fervently inquired, "Who composed these verses?" And the singer answered, "The Poet from Baalbek."

The Poet from Baalbek is an ancient name and it brought into the Prince's memory images of forgotten days. It awakened in the depth of his heart phantoms of remembrance, and drew before his eyes, with lines formed by the mist, a picture of a dead youth embracing his viol and surrounded by priests, chiefs, and ministers.

Like dreams dissipated by the light of Morn, the vision soon left the Prince's eyes. He stood up and walked toward his palace with crossed arms repeating the words of Mohammed, *"You were dead and He brought you back to life, and He will return you to the dead and then restore you to life. Whereupon you shall go back to Him."*

Then he looked at his boon companion and said, "We are fortunate to have the Poet from Baalbek in our land, and shall make it our paramount duty to honor and befriend him." After a few moments worthy of silence and respect, the Prince added in a low voice, "The poet is a bird of strange moods. He descends from his lofty domain to tarry among us, singing; if we do not honor him he will unfold his wings and fly back to his dwelling place."

The night was over, and the skies doffed their garments studded with stars, and put on raiment woven from the sinews of the rays of Morn. And the Prince's soul swayed between the wonders and strangeness of Existence and the concealed mysteries of Life.

The Return of the Beloved

❧

By nightfall the enemy fled with slashes of the sword and wounds of lance tips scarring their backs. Our heroes waved banners of triumph and chanted songs of victory to the cadence of their horses' hoofs that drummed upon the stones of the valley.

The moon had already risen from behind Fam El Mizab. The mighty and lofty rocks seemed to ascend with the spirits of the people, and the forest of cedars to lie like a medal of honor upon the bosom of Lebanon.

They continued their march, and the moon shone upon their weapons. The distant caves echoed their songs of praise and victory, until they reached the foot of a slope. There they were arrested by the neighing of a horse standing among gray rocks as though carved from them.

Near the horse they found a corpse, and the earth on which he lay was stained with his blood. The leader of the troop shouted, "Show me the man's sword and I will tell you who the owner is."

Some of the horsemen dismounted and surrounded the dead man and then one said to the chief, "His fingers have taken too strong a hold on the hilt. It would be a shame to undo them."

Another said, "The sword has been sheathed with escaping life that hides its metal."

A third one added, "The blood has congealed on both the hand and the hilt and made them one piece."

Whereupon the chief dismounted and walked to the corpse and said, "Raise his head and let the moon shine on his face so we may identify him." The men did as ordered, and the face of the slain man appeared from behind the veil of Death showing the marks of valor and nobility. It was the face of a strong horseman, and it bespoke manhood. It was the face of a sorrowing and rejoicing man; the face of one who had met the enemy courageously and faced death smilingly; the face of a Lebanese hero who, on that day, had witnessed the triumph but had not lived to march and sing and celebrate the victory with his comrades.

As they removed the silk head-wrapper and cleaned the dust of battle from his pale face, the chief cried out, in agony, "This is the son of Assaaby, what a great loss!" And the men repeated that name, sighing. Then silence fell upon them, and their hearts, intoxicated with the wine of victory, sobered. For they had seen something greater than the glory of triumph, in the loss of a hero.

Like statues of marble they stood in that scene of dread, and their taut tongues were mute and voiceless. This is what death does to the souls of heroes. Weeping and lamentation are for women; and moans and cries for children. Nothing befits the sorrow of men of the sword save silence which grips the strong heart as the eagle's talons grip the throat of its prey. It is that silence which rises above tears and wailing which, in its majesty, adds more awe and anguish to the misfortune; that silence which causes the soul to descend from the mountain-top into the abyss. It is the silence which proclaims the coming tempest. And when the tempest makes not its appearance, it is because the silence is stronger than the tempest.

They removed the raiment of the young hero to see where death had placed its iron claws. And the wounds appeared in his breast like speaking lips proclaiming, in the calmness of the night, the bravery of men.

The chief approached the corpse and dropped on his knees. Taking a closer look at the slain warrior, he found a scarf embroidered with gold threads tied around the arm. He recognized the hand that had spun its silk and the fingers that had woven its thread. He hid it under his raiment and withdrew slowly, hiding his stricken face with a trembling hand. Yet this trembling hand, with its might, had disjoined the heads of the enemy. Now it trembled because it had touched the edge of a scarf tied by loving fingers around the arm of a slain hero, who would return to her lifeless, borne upon the shoulders of his comrades.

While the leader's spirit wavered, considering both the tyranny of death and the secrets of love, one of the men suggested, "Let us dig a grave for him under that oak tree so that its roots may drink from his blood and its branches may receive nourishment from his remains. It will gain strength and become immortal and stand as a sign declaring to the hills and valleys his bravery and his might."

Another man said, "Let us carry him to the forest of the cedars and bury him by the church. There his bones will be eternally guarded by the shadow of the Cross."

And another said, "Bury him here where his blood is mingled with the earth. And let his sword remain in his right hand; plant his lance by his side and slay his horse over his grave and let his weapons be his cheer in his solitude."

But another objected, "Do not bury a sword stained with the enemy blood, nor slay a steed that has withstood death in the battle field. Do not leave in the wilderness weapons accustomed to action and strength, but carry them to his relatives as a great and good inheritance."

"Let us kneel down by his side and pray the Nazarene's prayers that God might forgive him and bless our victory," said another.

"Let us raise him upon our shoulders and make our shields and lances a bier for him and circle again this valley of our victory singing the songs of triumph so that the lips of his wounds will smile before they are muffled by the earth of the grave," said a comrade.

And another: "Let us mount him upon his charger and support him with the skulls of the dead enemy and gird him with his lance and bring him to the village a victor. He never yielded to death until he burdened it with the enemy's souls."

Another one said, "Come, let us bury him at the foot of this mountain. The echo of the caves shall be his companion and the murmur of the brook his minstrel. His bones shall rest in a wilderness where the tread of the silenced night is light and gentle."

Another objected, "No. Do not leave him in this place, for here dwells tedium and solitude. But let us carry him to the burial-ground of the village. The spirits of our forefathers will be his comrades and will speak to him in the silenced night and relate to him tales of their wars and sagas of their glory."

Then the chief walked to the center and motioned them to silence. He sighed and said, "Do not annoy him with memories of war or repeat to the ears of his soul, that hovers over us, the tales of swords and lances. Rather come and let us carry him calmly and silently to his birthplace, where a loving soul awaits his homecoming . . . a soul of a maiden awaiting his return from the battlefield. Let us return him to her so she may not be denied the sight of his face and the printing of a last kiss upon his forehead."

So they carried him upon their shoulders and walked silently with bent heads and downcast eyes. His sorrowful horse plodded behind them dragging its reins on the ground, uttering from time to time a desolate neighing echoed by the caves as if those caves had hearts and shared their grief.

Through the thorny path of the valley illuminated by a full moon, the procession of victory walked behind the cavalcade of Death and the spirit of Love led the way dragging his broken wings.

Union

❧

In this poem the Prophet of Lebanon appears to have previsioned the union of Egypt and Syria.

When the night had embellished heaven's garment with the stars' gems, there rose a houri from the Valley of the Nile and hovered in the sky on invisible wings. She sat upon a throne of mist hung between heaven and the sea. Before her passed a host of angels chanting in unison, "Holy, holy, holy· the daughter of Egypt whose grandeur fills the globe."

Then on the summit of Fam el Mizab, girdled by the forest of the cedars, a phantom youth was raised by the hands of the seraphim, and he sat upon the throne beside the houri. The spirits circled them singing, "Holy, holy, holy the youth of Lebanon, whose magnificence fills the ages."

And when the suitor held the hands of his beloved and gazed into her eyes, the wave and wind carried their communion to all the universe:

How faultless is your radiance, Oh daughter of Isis, and how great my adoration for you!

15

How graceful you are among the youths, Oh son of Astarte, and how great my yearning for you!

My love is as strong as your Pyramids, and the ages shall not destroy it.

My love is as staunch as your Holy Cedars, and the elements shall not prevail over it.

The wise men of all the nations come from East and West to discern your wisdom and to interpret your signs.

The scholars of the world come from all the kingdoms to intoxicate themselves with the nectar of your beauty and the magic of your voice.

Your palms are fountains of abundance.

Your arms are springs of pure water, and your breath is a refreshing breeze.

The palaces and temples of the Nile announce your glory, and the Sphinx narrates your greatness.

The cedars upon your bosom are like a medal of honor, and the towers about you speak your bravery and might.

Oh how sweet is your love and how wonderful is the hope that you foster.

Oh what a generous partner you are, and how faithful a spouse you have proved to be. How sublime are your gifts, and how precious your sacrifice!

You sent to me young men who were as an awakening after deep slumber. You gave me men of daring to conquer the weakness of my people, and scholars to exalt them, and geniuses to enrich their powers.

From the seeds I sent you you wrought flowers; from saplings you raised trees. For you are a virgin meadow on which roses and lilies grow and the cypresses and the cedar trees rise.

I see sorrow in your eyes, my beloved; do you grieve while you are at my side?

I have sons and daughters who emigrated beyond the seas and left me weeping and longing for their return.

Are you afraid, oh daughter of the Nile, and dearest of all nations?

I fear a tyrant approaching me with a sweet voice so that he may later rule me with the strength of his arms.

The life of the nations, my love, is like the life of individuals; a life cheered by Hope and married to Fear, beset by desires and frowned upon by Despair.

And the lovers embraced and kissed and drank from the cups of love the scented wine of the ages; and the host of spirits chanted, "Holy, holy, holy, Love's glory fills heaven and earth."

My Soul Preached to Me

My soul preached to me and taught me to love that which the people abhor and befriend him whom they revile.

My soul showed me that Love prides itself not only in the one who loves, but also in the beloved.

Ere my soul preached to me, Love was in my heart as a tiny thread fastened between two pegs.

But now Love has become a halo whose beginning is its end, and whose end is its beginning. It surrounds every being and extends slowly to embrace all that shall be.

My soul advised me and taught me to perceive the hidden beauty of the skin, figure, and hue. She instructed me to meditate upon that which the people call ugly until its true charm and delight appear.

Ere my soul counselled me, I saw Beauty like a trembling torch between columns of smoke. Now since the smoke has vanished, I see naught save the flame.

My soul preached to me and taught me to listen to

the voices which the tongue and the larynx and the lips do not utter.

Ere my soul preached to me, I heard naught but clamor and wailing. But now I eagerly attend Silence and hear its choirs singing the hymns of the ages and the songs of the firmament announcing the secrets of the Unseen.

My soul preached to me and instructed me to drink the wine that cannot be pressed and cannot be poured from cups that hands can lift or lips can touch.

Ere my soul preached to me, my thirst was like a dim spark hidden under the ashes that can be extinguished by a swallow of water.

But now my longing has become my cup, my affections my wine, and my loneliness my intoxication: yet, in this unquenchable thirst there is eternal joy.

My soul preached to me and taught me to touch that which has not become incarnate; my soul revealed to me that whatever we touch is part of our desire.

But now my fingers have turned into mist penetrating that which is seen in the universe and mingling with the Unseen.

My soul instructed me to inhale the scent that no myrtle or incense emits. Ere my soul preached to me, I craved the scent of perfume in the gardens or in flasks or in censers.

But now I can savor the incense that is not burnt for offering or sacrifice. And I fill my heart with a fragrance that has never been wafted by the frolicsome breeze of space.

My soul preached to me and taught me to say, "I am ready" when the Unknown and Danger call on me.

Ere my soul preached to me, I answered no voice save the voice of the crier whom I knew, and walked not save upon the easy and smooth path.

Now the Unknown has become a steed that I can mount in order to reach the Unknown; and the plain has turned into a ladder on whose steps I climb to the summit.

My soul spoke to me and said, "Do not measure Time by saying, 'There was yesterday, and there shall be tomorrow.'"

And ere my soul spoke to me, I imagined the Past as an epoch that never returned, and the Future as one that could never be reached.

Now I realize that the present moment contains all time and within it is all that can be hoped for, done and realized.

My soul preached to me exhorting me not to limit space by saying, "Here, there, and yonder."

Ere my soul preached to me, I felt that wherever I walked was far from any other space.

Now I realize that wherever I am contains all places; and the distance that I walk embraces all distances.

My soul instructed me and advised me to stay

awake while others sleep. And to surrender to slumber when others are astir.

Ere my soul preached to me, I saw not their dreams in my sleep, neither did they observe my vision.

Now I never sail the vessel of my dreams unless they watch me, and they never soar into the sky of their vision unless I rejoice in their freedom.

My soul preached to me and said, "Do not be delighted because of praise, and do not be distressed because of blame."

Ere my soul counselled me, I doubted the worth of my work.

Now I realize that the trees blossom in Spring and bear fruit in Summer without seeking praise; and they drop their leaves in Autumn and become naked in Winter without fearing blame.

My soul preached to me and showed me that I am neither more than the pygmy, nor less than the giant.

Ere my soul preached to me, I looked upon humanity as two men: one weak, whom I pitied, and the other strong, whom I followed or resisted in defiance.

But now I have learned that I was as both are and made from the same elements. My origin is their origin, my conscience is their conscience, my contention is their contention, and my pilgrimage is their pilgrimage.

If they sin, I am also a sinner. If they do well, I take pride in their well-doing. If they rise, I rise with them. If they stay inert, I share their slothfulness.

My soul spoke to me and said, "The lantern which you carry is not yours, and the song that you sing was not composed within your heart, for even if you bear the light, you are not the light, and even if you are a lute fastened with strings, you are not the lute player."

My soul preached to me, my brother, and taught me much. And your soul has preached and taught as much to you. For you and I are one, and there is no variance between us save that I urgently declare that which is in my inner self, while you keep as a secret that which is within you. But in your secrecy there is a sort of virtue.

The Sons of the Goddess
and the Sons of the Monkeys

❧

How strange Time is, and how queer we are! Time has really changed, and lo, it has changed us too. It walked one step forward, unveiled its face, alarmed us and then elated us.

Yesterday we complained about Time and trembled at its terrors. But today we have learned to love it and revere it, for we now understand its intents, its natural disposition, its secrets, and its mysteries.

Yesterday we crawled in fright like shuddering ghosts between the fears of the night and the menaces of the day. But today we walk joyously towards the mountain peak, the dwelling place of the raging tempest and the birthplace of thunder.

Yesterday we ate our bread kneaded with blood, and we drank our water mixed with tears. But today we began to receive the manna from the hands of the morning brides and drank the aged wine scented with the sweet breath of Spring.

Yesterday we were a toy in the hands of Destiny. But today Destiny has awakened from her intoxication to play and laugh and walk with us. We do not follow her but she follows us.

Yesterday we burned incense before the idols and offered sacrifices to the angry gods. But today we burn incense and offer sacrifices to our own being, for the greatest and most beautiful of all gods has raised his temple in our hearts.

Yesterday we bowed to the kings and bent our necks to the sultans. But today we do not pay reverence save to Right and we follow no one except Beauty and Love.

Yesterday we honored false prophets and sorcerers. But today Time has changed, and lo, it has changed us too. We can now stare at the face of the sun and listen to the songs of the sea, and nothing can shake us except a cyclone.

Yesterday we tore down the temples of our souls and from their debris we built tombs for our forefathers. But today our souls have turned into sacred altars that the ghosts of the Past cannot approach, that the fleshless fingers of the dead cannot touch.

We were a silent thought hidden in the corners of Oblivion. Today we are a strong voice that can make the firmament reverberate.

We were a tiny spark buried under the ashes. Today we are a raging fire burning at the head of the valley.

We spent many a night awake, with the earth as our pillow and the snow as our blanket.

Like sheep without a shepherd we flocked together

many nights grazing on our thoughts, and chewing the cud of our emotions; yet we remained hungry and athirst.

Oftentime we stood between a passing day and a coming night lamenting our withering youth and longing for someone unknown, and gazing at the void and dark sky listening to the moaning of Silence and the shrieking of nothingness.

Those ages passed like wolves among the graves. But today the skies are clear, and we can rest peacefully upon divine beds and welcome our thoughts and dreams, and embrace our desires. Grasping with untrembling fingers the torches that sway around us, we can talk to the genii with explicit meaning. As the choirs of angels pass us, they become intoxicated with the longing of our hearts and the hymns of our souls.

Yesterday we were, and today we are! This is the will of the goddess among the sons of the goddess. What is your will, oh sons of the monkeys? Have you walked a single step forward since you came forth from the crevices of the earth? Have you gazed toward heaven since Satan opened your eyes? Have you uttered a word from the book of Right since the lips of vipers kissed your lips? Or have you listened a moment to the song of Life since Death closed your ears?

Seventy thousand years ago I passed by and saw you moving like insects inside the caves; and seven minutes ago I glanced at you through the crystal glass

of my window and saw you walking through the alleys
fettered by slavery while the wings of Death hovered
over you. You look the same today as you looked
yesterday; and tomorrow, and the day after it, you
shall look as I saw you in the beginning.

Yesterday we were, and today we are! This is the
will of the goddess among the sons of the goddess;
what is your will, oh sons of the monkeys?

Decayed Teeth

※

I had a decayed tooth in my mouth that troubled me. It stayed dormant during the day. But in the tranquility of the night, when the dentists were asleep and drug stores closed, it began to ache.

One day, as I grew impatient, I went to the dentist and told him to extract that damned tooth that dealt me misery and denied me the joy of slumber by converting the silence of my night into moaning and uproar.

The dentist shook his head and said, "It is foolish to have your tooth extracted if we can cure it."

Then he started to drill its sides and clean its cavities and used every means to restore it and free it from decay. Having finished drilling, he filled it with pure gold and said boastfully, "Your bad tooth now is stronger and more solid than your good ones." I believed him and paid him and departed from the place.

But before the week was over, the cursed tooth returned to its diseased condition and the torture it inflicted converted the beautiful songs of my soul into wailing and agony.

So I went to another dentist and said to him, "Extract this damned tooth without asking me any question, for the person who receives the blows is not like the one who counts them."

Obeying my command, he extracted the tooth. Looking at it he said, "You have done well to have this rotten tooth extracted."

In the mouth of Society are many diseased teeth, decayed to the bones of the jaws. But Society makes no efforts to have them extracted and be rid of the affliction. It contents itself with gold fillings. Many are the dentists who treat the decayed teeth of Society with glittering gold.

Numerous are those who yield to the enticements of such reformers, and pain, sickness, and death are their lot.

In the mouth of the Syrian nation are many rotten, black, and dirty teeth that fester and stink. The doctors have attempted cures with gold fillings instead of extraction. And the disease remains.

A nation with rotten teeth is doomed to have a sick stomach. Many are the nations afflicted with such indigestion.

If you wish to take a look at the decayed teeth of Syria, visit its schools where the sons and daughters of today are preparing to become the men and women of tomorrow.

Visit the courts and witness the acts of the crooked and corrupted purveyors of justice. See how they play with the thoughts and minds of the simple people as a cat plays with a mouse.

Visit the homes of the rich where conceit, falsehood, and hypocrisy reign.

But don't neglect to go through the huts of the poor as well, where dwell fear, ignorance, and cowardice.

Then visit the nimble-fingered dentists, possessors of delicate instruments, dental plasters and tranquilizers, who spend their days filling the cavities in the rotten teeth of the nation to mask the decay.

Talk to those reformers who pose as the intelligentsia of the Syrian nation and organize societies, hold conferences, and deliver public speeches. When you talk to them you will hear tunes that perhaps sound more sublime than the grinding of a millstone, and nobler than the croaking of frogs on a June night.

When you tell them the Syrian nation gnaws its bread with decayed teeth and each morsel it chews is mixed with poisoned saliva that spreads diseases in the nation's stomach, they answer, "Yes, but we are seeking better tooth fillings and tranquilizers."

And if you suggest "extraction" to them, they will laugh at you because you have not yet learned the noble art of dentistry that conceals disease.

If you were to insist, they would go off and shun you, saying to themselves:

"Many are the idealists in this world, and weak are their dreams."

Mister Gabber

❧

I am bored with gabbers and their gab; my soul abhors them.

When I wake up in the morning to peruse the letters and magazines placed by my bedside, I find them full of gab; all I see is loose talk empty of meaning but stuffed with hypocrisy.

When I sit by the window to lower the veil of slumber from my eyes and sip my Turkish coffee, Mister Gabber appears before me, hopping, crying, and grumbling. He condescends to sip my coffee and smoke my cigarettes.

When I go to work Mister Gabber follows, whispering in my ears and tickling my sensitive brain. When I try to get rid of him he giggles and is soon midstream again, in his flood of meaningless talk.

When I go to the market, Mister Gabber stands at the door of every shop passing judgment on people. I see him even upon the faces of the silent for he accompanies them too. They are unaware of his presence, yet he disturbs them.

If I sit down with a friend Mister Gabber, uninvited, makes a third. If I elude him, he manages to remain so close that the echo of his voice irritates me and upsets my stomach like spoiled meat.

When I visit the courts and the institutions of learning, I find him and his father and mother dressing Falsehood in silky garments and Hypocrisy in a magnificent cloak and a beautiful turban.

When I call at factory offices, there too, to my surprise, I find Mister Gabber, in the midst of his mother, aunt, and grandfather chattering and flapping his thick lips. And his kinfolks applaud him and mock me.

On my visit to the temples and other places of worship, there he is, seated on a throne, his head crowned and a gleaming sceptre in his hand.

Returning home at eventide, I find him there, too. From the ceiling he hangs like a snake; or crawls like a boa in the four corners of my house.

In short, Mister Gabber is found everywhere; within and beyond the skies, on land and underground, on the wings of the ether and upon the waves of the sea, in the forests, in the caves, and on the mountaintops.

Where can a lover of silence and tranquility find rest from him? Will God ever have mercy on my soul and grant me the grace of dumbness so I may reside in the paradise of Silence?

Is there in this universe a nook where I can go and live happily by myself?

Is there any place where there is no traffic in empty talk?

Is there on this earth one who does not worship himself talking?

Is there any person among all persons whose mouth is not a hiding place for the knavish Mister Gabber?

If there were but one kind of gabber, I would be resigned. But gabbers are innumerable. They can be divided into clans and tribes:

There are those who live in marshes all day long, but when night comes, they move to the banks and raise their heads out of the water and the slime, and fill the silent night with horrible croaking that bursts the eardrums.

There are those who belong to the family of gnats. It is they who hover around our heads and make tiny devilish noises out of spite and hatred.

There is the clan whose members swill brandy and beer and stand at the street corners and fill the ether with a bellowing thicker than a buffalo's wallow.

We see also a queer tribe of people who pass their time at the tombs of Life converting silence into a sort of wailing more lugubrious than the screeching of the owl.

Then there is the gang of gabbers who imagine life as a piece of lumber from which they try to shape something for themselves, raising as they do so, a screeching sound uglier than the din of a sawmill.

Following this gang is a denomination of creatures who pound themselves with mallets to produce hollow tones more awful than the tomtoms of jungle savages.

Supporting these creatures is a sect whose members have nothing to do save to sit down, whenever a seat is available, and there chew words instead of uttering them.

Once in a while we find a party of gabbers who weave air from air, but remain without a garment.

Oftentime we run across a unique order of gabbers whose representatives are like starlings but deem themselves eagles when they soar in the currents of their words.

And what of those gabbers who are like ringing bells calling the people to worship but who never enter the church.

There are still more tribes and clans of gabbers, but they are too many to enumerate. Of these the strangest, in my opinion, is a sleeping denomination whose members trouble the universe with their snoring and awaken themselves, from time to time, to say, "How erudite we are!"

Having expressed my abhorrence of Mister Gabber and his comrades, I find myself like the doctor who cannot heal himself, or like a convict preaching to his cellmates. I have satirized Mister Gabber and his gabbing friends—with my own gabbing. I have fled from gabbers but I am one of them.

Will God ever forgive my sins before He blesses me and places me in the world of Thought, Truth, and Affection, where gabbers do not exist?

In the Dark Night

Written in World War I during the famine in Lebanon

In the dark night we call to one another and cry for help, while the ghost of Death stands in our midst stretching his black wings over us and, with his iron hands, pushes our souls into the abyss.

In the dark night Death strides on and we follow him frightened and moaning. Not one of us is capable of halting the fateful procession or even nourishing a hope of its end.

In the dark night Death walks and we walk behind him. And when he looks backward, hundreds of souls fall down on both sides of the road. And he who falls, sleeps and never awakens. And he who keeps his footing marches on fearfully in the dread certainty of falling later and joining those who have yielded to Death and entered the eternal sleep. But Death marches on, gazing at the distant Evening Twilight.

In the dark night the brother calls his brother, the father his son, and the mother her children; but the pangs and torments of hunger afflict us equally.

But Death does not hunger or thirst. He devours our souls and bodies, drinks our blood and tears and is never sated.

During the first part of the night the child calls his mother saying, "I am hungry, mother," and the mother replies, "Wait a while, my child."

In the second part of the night the child repeats, "I am hungry, mother, give me some bread," and the mother answers him, saying, "I have no bread, my beloved child."

In the third part of the night Death arrives and smites both the mother and the child with his wings and they both sleep eternally by the side of the road. And Death marches on, gazing at the distant Evening Twilight.

In the morn the husband goes to the field in search of nourishment, but he finds naught in it save dust and stones.

At noontide he returns to his wife and children pale, weak, and empty-handed.

And at eventide Death arrives and the husband, his wife, and children lie in eternal sleep. And he laughs and marches on toward the distant Evening Twilight.

In the morn the farmer leaves his hut for the city, carrying in his pocket his mother's and sisters' jewelry to exchange for bread. At eventide he returns without bread and without jewels, to find his mother and sisters sunk into eternal sleep, their eyes staring at nothingness. Whereupon he lifts his arms toward heaven and drops like a bird shot by a merciless hunter.

And Death, seeing the farmer, his mother and sisters beguiled to eternal sleep by the evil angel, laughs again and marches on toward the distant Evening Twilight.

Oh, you who walk in the light of the day, we call you from the endless dark of the night. Do you hear our cries?

We have sent to you the spirits of our dead as our apostles. Have you heeded the apostles' word?

We have burdened the East Wind with our gasps. Has the Wind reached your distant shores to unload his burden in your hands? Are you aware of our misery? Have you thought of coming to our rescue? Or have you hugged to yourselves your peace and comfort, saying, "What can the sons of the light do for the sons of the dark? Let the dead bury their dead and God's will be done."

Yes, let God's will be done. But can you not raise yourselves above yourselves so that God may make you instruments of His will and use you for our aid?

In the dark night we call one another.

The brother calls his brother, the mother her daughter, the man his wife, and the lover his beloved.

And when our voices mingle together and reach the heart of heaven, Death pauses and laughs, then mocks us and marches on, gazing at the distant Evening Twilight.

The Silver-Plated Turd

❧

Silman Effandi is a well-dressed man, tall and hand-some, thirty-five years of age. He curls his mustaches and wears silk socks and patent-leather shoes. In his soft and delicate hand he carries a gold-headed and bejewelled walking stick. He eats in the most expensive restaurants where the fashionable forgather. In his magnificent carriage, drawn by thoroughbreds, he rides through the upper-class boulevards.

Silman Effandi's wealth was not inherited from his father, who (may his soul rest in peace) was a poor man. Neither did Silman Effandi amass wealth by shrewd and persevering business activities. He is lazy and hates to work, regarding any form of labor as degrading.

Once we heard him say, "My physique and temperament unfit me for work; work is meant for those with sluggish character and brutish body."

Then how did Silman attain his riches? By what magic was the dirt in his hands transformed into gold and silver? This is a secret hidden in a silver-plated turd which Azrael, the angel of Death, has revealed to us, and we in turn shall reveal it to you:

Five years ago Silman Effandi married the lady Faheema, widow of Betros Namaan, famous for his honesty, perseverance, and hard work.

Faheema was then forty-five years of age, but only sweet sixteen in her thoughts and behavior. She now dyes her hair and by the use of cosmetics deludes herself that she remains young and beautiful. She does not see Silman, her young husband, except after midnight when he vouchsafes her a scornful look and some vulgarities and abuse by way of conversation. This entitles him, he believes, to spend the money which her first husband earned by the sweat of his brow.

Adeeb Effandi is a young man, twenty-seven years of age, blessed with a big nose, small eyes, dirty face and ink-spotted hands with filth-encrusted fingernails. His clothes are frayed and adorned with oil, grease and coffee stains.

His ugly appearance is not due to Adeeb Effandi's poverty but to his preoccupation with spiritual and theological ideas. He often quotes Ameen El Jundy's saying that a scholar cannot be both clean and intelligent.

In his incessant talk Adeeb Effandi has nothing to say except to deliver judgment on others. On investigation, we found that Adeeb Effandi had spent two years in a school at Beirut studying rhetoric. He wrote poems, essays, and articles, which never saw print. His reasons for failing to achieve publication are the degeneration of the Arabic press and the ignorance of the Arabic reading public.

Recently Adeeb Effandi has been occupying himself with the study of the old and new philosophy. He admires Socrates and Nietzsche, and relishes the sayings of Saint Augustine as well as Voltaire and Rousseau. At a wedding party we heard him discussing Hamlet; but his talk was a soliloquy, for the others preferred to drink and sing.

On another occasion, at a funeral, the subjects of his talk were the love poems of Ben Al Farid and the wine-ism of Abi Nawaas. But the mourners ignored him, being oppressed by grief.

Why, we often wonder, does Adeeb Effandi exist? What use are his rotting books and his parchments falling into dust? Would it not be better for him to buy himself an ass and become a healthy and useful assdriver?

This is a secret hidden in the silver-plated turd revealed to us by Baal-Zabul and we in turn shall now reveal it to you:

Three years ago Adeeb Effandi composed a poem in praise of His Excellency, Bishop Joseph Shamoun. His Excellency placed his hand on the shoulder of Adeeb Effandi, smiled and said, "Bravo, my son, God bless you! I have no doubt about your intelligence; some day you will be among the great men of the East."

Fareed Bey Davis is a man in his late thirties, tall,

with a small head and large mouth, narrow forehead and a bald pate. He walks with a pompous rolling gait, swelling his chest and stretching his long neck like a camel.

From his loud voice and his haughty manner you might imagine him (provided you had not met him before) the minister of a great empire, absorbed in public affairs.

But Fareed has nothing to do aside from enumerating and glorifying the deeds of his ancestors. He is fond of citing exploits of famous men, and deeds of heroes such as Napoleon and Antar. He is a collector of weapons of which he has never learned the use.

One of his sayings is that God created two different classes of people: the leaders and those who serve them. Another is that the people are like stubborn asses who do not stir unless you whip them. Another, that the pen was meant for the weak and the sword for the strong.

What prompts Fareed to boast of his ancestry and behave as he does? This is a secret hidden in the silver-plated turd which Satanael has revealed to us, and we, in turn, reveal to you:

In the third decade of the nineteenth century when Emeer Basheer, the great Governor of Mount Lebanon, was passing with his retinue through the Lebanese valleys, they approached the village in which Mansour Davis, Fareed's grandfather lived. It was an exceedingly hot day, and the Emeer dismounted from his horse and ordered his men to rest in the shadow of an oak tree.

Mansour Davis, discovering the Emeer's presence, called the neighboring farmers, and the good news spread through the village. Led by Mansour the villagers brought baskets of grapes and figs, and jars of honey, wine and milk for the Emeer. When they reached the oak tree, Mansour kneeled before the Emeer and kissed the hem of his robe. Then he stood up and killed a sheep in the Emeer's honor, saying, "The sheep is from thy bounty, oh Prince and protector of our lives." The Emeer, pleased with such hospitality, said to him, "Henceforth you shall be the mayor of this village which I will exempt from taxes for this year."

That night, after the Emeer had left, the villagers met at the house of "Sheik" Mansour Davis and vowed loyalty to the newly appointed Sheik. May God have mercy on their souls.

There are too many secrets contained in the silver-plated turd to enumerate them all. The devils and satans reveal some to us every day and night, which we shall share with you before the angel of death wraps us under his wings and takes us into the Great Beyond.

Since it is now midnight and our eyes are getting heavy, permit us to surrender ourselves to Slumber and perhaps the beautiful bride of dreams will carry our souls into a world cleaner than this one.

Martha

❧

I

Her father died when she was in the cradle, and she lost her mother before reaching the age of ten. As an orphan, Martha was left in the care of a poor peasant whose servant she became. They lived in an obscure hamlet on a slope of the beautiful mountains of North Lebanon.

At his death, her father had left his family only his good name and a hut standing amidst willow and walnut trees. It was the death of her mother which truly orphaned her. It left an emptiness in her heart which could not be filled. She became a stranger in her birthplace. Every day she walked barefoot leading a cow to pasture. While the cow grazed she sat under a tree, singing with the birds, weeping with the stream, envying the cow her serenity, and gazing at the flowers over which the butterflies hovered.

At night she returned home to a simple dinner of bread, olives, and dried fruit. She slept in a bed of straw, with her arms for a pillow; and it was her prayer that her whole life might be uninterrupted slumber. At dawn her master would wake her so that she would get the housework done before she led the cow to pasture. She trembled and did as she was ordered.

Thus the gloomy and puzzling years passed, and Martha grew like a sapling. In her heart there developed a quiet affection of which she herself was unaware . . . like fragrance born in the heart of a flower. She followed her fancy as sheep follow a stream to quench their thirst. Her mind was like virgin land where knowledge had sown no seeds and upon which no feet had trod.

We who live amid the excitements of the city know nothing of the life of the mountain villagers. We are swept into the current of urban existence, until we forget the peaceful rhythms of simple country life, which smiles in the spring, toils in summer, reaps in autumn, rests in winter, imitating nature in all her cycles. We are wealthier than the villagers in silver or gold, but they are richer in spirit. What we sow we reap not; they reap what they sow. We are slaves of gain, and they the children of contentment. Our draught from the cup of life is mixed with bitterness and despair, fear and weariness; but they drink the pure nectar of life's fulfillment.

At sixteen, Martha's soul was like a clear mirror that reflects a beautiful landscape; her heart like a primeval valley that echoes all voices.

One day in autumn she sat by the spring, gazing at the falling yellow leaves, stripped from the trees by the breeze that moved between the branches as death moves into a man's soul. She looked at the withering flowers whose hearts were dry and whose seeds sought shelter in earth's bosom like refugees seeking a new life.

While thus engrossed, she heard hoofbeats upon the ground. Turning, she observed a horseman approaching. As he reached the spring he dismounted and greeted her with kind words, such as she had not heard from a man before. Then he went on to say, "Young lady, I have lost my way. Will you please direct me to the road to the coast?"

Looking like a tender branch, there by the spring, she replied, "I regret, sir, that I am unable to direct you, never having been away from home; but if you will ask my master I am sure he can help you." Her flushed face, as she spoke, made her look more gentle and beautiful. As she started away he stopped her. His expression became soft as he said, "Please do not go."

And a strange power in the man's voice held her immobile. When she stole a glance at his face she found him gazing at her steadily. She could not understand his silent adoration.

He eyed her lovely bare feet, her graceful arms and smooth neck and shining hair. Lovingly and wonderingly he regarded her sun-warmed cheeks and her chiseled features. She could not utter a single word or move a muscle.

The cow returned alone to the barn that evening. Martha's master searched all through the valley but could not find her. His wife wept all that night. She said the next morning, "I saw Martha in my dream last night, and she was between the paws of a wild beast who lured her; the beast was about to kill Martha, but she smiled."

II

In the autumn of 1900, after a vacation in North Lebanon, I returned to Beyrouth. Before re-entering school I spent a week roaming the city with my classmates. We were like birds whose cage-door is unlocked, and who come and go as they please.

Youth is a beautiful dream, on whose brightness books shed a blinding dust. Will ever the day come when the wise link the joy of knowledge to youth's dream? Will ever the day come when Nature becomes the teacher of man, humanity his book and life his school? Youth's joyous purpose cannot be fulfilled until that day comes. Too slow is our march toward spiritual elevation, because we make so little use of youth's ardor.

One evening, as I was contemplating the jostling street crowds of Beyrouth, and feeling deafened by the shouts of the street vendors, I noticed a ragged boy of about five carrying some flowers on a tray. In a dispirited voice he asked me, "Will you buy some flowers, sir?" His mouth was half-open, resembling and echoing a deep wound in the soul. His arms were thin and bare, and his frail body was bent over his flower tray like a branch of withering roses.

In my reply I tried to keep from my voice any intrusive edge of charity.

I bought some of his flowers but my chief purpose was to converse with him. I felt that his heart was a stage upon which a continuous drama of misery was being enacted.

At my careful, tactful words he began to feel secure and a smile brightened his face. He was surprised to hear words of kindness, for like all the poor he was accustomed to harshness. I asked his name, which was Fu'ad, and then, "Whose son are you?" He replied, "I am the son of Martha." "And who is your father?" I inquired. He shook his head, puzzled, as if unaware of the meaning of the word. I continued, "Where is your mother now, Fu'ad?" He replied, weeping, "She is at home, sick."

Suddenly remembrance formed in my mind. Martha, whose unfinished story I had heard from an old villager, was ill nearby. That young woman who yesterday safely roamed the valley and enjoyed the beauty of nature was now suffering the anguish of destitution; that orphan who spent her early life in the haven of Nature was undergoing the tortures that city sophistication inflicts upon the innocent.

As the boy started to leave, I took hold of his hand saying, "Take me to your mother. I would like to see her." He led the way silently, looking back now and then to see if I followed.

Through narrow, dirty streets with an odor of death in the air, and between houses of ill-fame, raucous with the sounds of sin, I walked behind Fu'ad, admiring the courage in his stride. It took courage to walk in these slums, where violence, crime and plague mocked the glory of this city, called "The Bride of Syria" and "The Pearl of the Sultan's Crown."

As we entered a particularly squalid quarter, the boy pointed to a hovel whose walls appeared to be collapsing. My heartbeats quickened and I followed Fu'ad into a sunless, airless room, unfurnished except for an oil lamp and a hard bed upon which Martha was lying, her face to the wall as if to hide from the oppression of the city. Fu'ad touched her shoulder and said, "Mama." As she turned painfully, he pointed at me. She moved her weak body under the ragged quilt, and with a despairing voice said, "What brings you here, stranger? What do you want? Did you come here to buy the last remnant of my soul and pollute it with your desire? Go away from here; the streets are full of women who sell themselves. What is left of my broken soul death shall soon buy. Go away from me and my boy."

Those few words completed her tragic story. I said, "Fear me not, Martha; I come here not as a devourer, but as a fellow sufferer. I am a Lebanese who lived near your valley by the cedars of Lebanon. Do not be frightened."

Realizing then that my words came from a feeling soul, she shook like a thin branch before a strong wind, and placed her hands upon her face, trying to hide away the terrible and beautiful memory whose sweetness was ravaged by bitterness.

Then in a strangely strong yet hopeless voice she said, "You have come here as a benefactor, and may God reward you; but I beg you to leave, for your presence here will bring disgrace upon you. Avoid being recognized. Your merciful heart does not restore my virtue; it neither effaces my shame nor protects me from the hands of death. My own sin brought this misery upon me; do not let your mercy bring you into shame. I am like a leper who must be avoided. Go, lest you be polluted! Do not mention my name in North Lebanon. The lamb with the mange is destroyed by the shepherd for fear he will infect the other lambs. If you speak of me, say I am dead."

Then she embraced her little boy and said: "People will taunt my son, saying he is the fruit of sin; the son of Martha the adulteress; Martha the prostitute. For they are blind and do not see that his mother gave him life through misery. I shall die and leave him as an orphan among other children, and his remembrance of me will bring him shame. But when he becomes a man, he will help heaven to end that which brought sin upon me; and when he dies in the trap of time, he will find me waiting for him in Eternity, where light and peace abide."

With a desolate heart I said, "Martha, you are not a leper. You live in a grave yet you are clean. The filth of the body cannot reach a pure soul."

Hearing my heartfelt words, Martha's face brightened. But it was plain that her death was near. Yesterday she had roamed the valleys of Lebanon; today, weak and sorrowful, she awaited release from the shackles of life. Gathering her last fragments of strength she whispered, "I am everything you say, although my own weakness brought my agony . . . the horseman came . . . he spoke politely and cleverly . . . he kissed me . . . I knew nothing and relied on his words. He took me away and his fine words and smiles masked his ugly desires. After accomplishing my disgrace, he abandoned me. He split my life in two parts —my helpless self, and my baby. We were cold . . . we suffered. . . . For the sake of my child I took gold from men who bought my body. Many times I was close to taking my life. Now, at last, the hour has come and beloved death has arrived to enfold me under his sheltering wings."

Suddenly in a strong but calm voice she said, "Oh Justice, hidden behind those terrible images, hear the shrieking of my departing soul and the call of my broken heart! Have mercy on me by saving my child and taking me away!"

Her breathing became weak. She looked sorrowfully and sweetly at her son and then whispered, "Our Father which art in heaven, hallowed be Thy name. Thy kingdom come, Thy will be done on earth as it is in heaven. . . . Forgive us our sins as we . . ."

Her voice gave out but her lips still moved. Then she breathed her last on earth. Her eyes remained open as if seeing the invisible.

As dawn came, the body of Martha was carried in a rough casket to a graveyard by two poor men. Far out from the City of Beyrouth they carried her. The priests refused to pray for her, and prohibited her interment in hallowed ground. And no one accompanied Martha to her resting place except her little son Fu'ad and a youth to whom life had taught mercy and kindness.

Vision

❧

When Night came and Slumber spread its garment upon the face of the earth, I left my bed and walked toward the sea saying, "The sea never sleeps, and in its vigil there is consolation for a sleepless soul."

When I reached the shore, the mist from the mountains had engauzed the region as a veil adorns the face of a young woman. I gazed at the teeming waves and listened to their praise of God and meditated upon the eternal power hidden within them—that power which runs with the tempest and rises with the volcano and smiles through the lips of the roses and sings with the brooks.

Then I saw three phantoms sitting upon a rock. I stumbled toward them as if some power were pulling me against my will.

Within a few paces from the phantoms, I halted as though held still by a magic force. At that moment one of the phantoms stood up and in a voice that seemed to rise from the depth of the sea said:

"Life without Love is like a tree without blossom

and fruit. And love without Beauty is like flowers without scent and fruits without seeds. . . . Life, Love, and Beauty are three persons in one, who cannot be separated or changed."

A second phantom spoke with a voice that roared like cascading water and said:

"Life without Rebellion is like seasons without Spring. And Rebellion without Right is like Spring in an arid desert. . . . Life, Rebellion, and Right are three-in-one who cannot be changed or separated."

Then the third phantom in a voice like a clap of thunder spoke:

"Life without Freedom is like a body without a soul, and Freedom without Thought is like a confused spirit. . . . Life, Freedom, and Thought are three-in-one, and are everlasting and never pass away."

Then the three phantoms stood up together, and with one tremendous voice said:

> "That which Love begets,
> That which Rebellion creates,
> That which Freedom rears,
> Are three manifestations of God.
> And God is the expression
> Of the intelligent Universe."

At that moment Silence mingled with the rustling of invisible wings and trembling of ethereal bodies; and it prevailed.

I closed my eyes and listened to the echoes of the sayings which I had just heard, and when I opened them I saw nothing but the sea wreathed in mist. I walked toward the rock where the three phantoms were sitting, but I saw naught save a column of incense spiralling toward heaven.

Communion of Spirits

Awake, my love, awake! For my spirit hails you from beyond the seas, and offers you her wings above the raging waves.

Awake, for silence has halted the clamor of the horses' hoofs and the tramp of the passers-by.

Slumber has embraced the spirits of men, while I alone remain awake; longing lifts me out of enveloping sleep.

Love brings me close to you but then, anxiety takes me far away.

I have left my bed, my love, for fear of the ghost of forgetfulness hiding in the quilts.

I have thrown my book aside, for my sighs silenced the words and left the pages blank before my eyes!

Awake, awake, my love, and hear me.

I hear you, my beloved! I heard your call from beyond the seas and felt the soft touch of your wings. I have left my bed and walked upon the grass and the night dew has wet my feet and the hem of my garment. Here I stand under the blossoms of the almond tree, heeding the call of your spirit.

Speak to me, my love, and let your breath mount the breeze that comes towards me from the valleys of Lebanon. Speak. No one hears but me. Night has taken all others to their resting places.

Heaven has woven a veil of moonlight and drawn it over all Lebanon, my beloved.

Heaven has fashioned from the shadows of night a thick cloak lined with the fumes of workshops and the breath of Death, and laid it over the frame of the city, my love.

The villagers have surrendered to Slumber in their huts in the midst of the willow and walnut trees. Their spirits have sped towards the land of dreams, my beloved.

Men are bent under the burden of gold, and the steep road of green weakens their knees. Their eyes are heavy with trouble and weariness, and they drop on their beds as a haven, my love, from the Ghosts of Fear and Despair.

The ghosts of past ages walk in the valleys, and the spirits of the kings and prophets hover over the knolls and the hills. And my thoughts, fashioned by memory, show me the might of the Chaldeans, the splendor of the Assyrians, and the nobility of the Arabs.

In the sinister alleys walk the grim spirits of the thieves; the heads of the vipers of lust appear from the crevices of the ramparts; and the ague of sickness, mingled with the agony of Death, shudders through the streets. Memory has removed the veil of forgetfulness from my eyes and shows me the loathsomeness of Sodom and the sins of Gomorrah.

The branches sway, my beloved, and their rustling joins the murmur of the rivulet in the valley, repeating to our ears the canticles of Solomon, the strains of David's harp, and the songs of Ishak al-Mausili.

The souls of the hungry children in the lodgings tremble; and the sighs of the mothers tossing upon the beds of misery and despair have reached the sky; and anxious dreams afflict the hearts of the infirm. I hear their bitter lamentations.

The fragrance of flowers has mingled with the pungent breath of the cedars. Brought by the frolicsome breeze over the hills, it fills the soul with affection and inspires longing for flight.

But the miasmas from the marshes also rise, steaming with disease. Like sharp secret arrows they have penetrated the senses and poisoned the air.

The morning has come, my beloved, and the soft fingers of wakefulness fondle the eyes of the dreamers. Rays of light force open the shutters and reveal Life's resolution and glory. The villages, reposing in peace and tranquility upon the shoulders of the valley, rise from their slumber; church bells fill the air with their pleasing summons to morning prayer. And from the caves echo the chimes as if all Nature joins in reverent prayer. The calves have left their stalls, and the sheep and the goats their sheds, to graze upon the glittering, dewy grass. The shepherds walk before them, piping on their reeds; and behind them walk the damsels singing like the birds welcoming the morn.

And now the heavy hand of the Day lies upon the city. The curtains have been drawn from the windows and the doors are open. The fatigued eyes and drawn faces of toilers appear in the workshops. They feel death encroaching upon their lives, and on their shrivelled countenances appear Fear and Despair. The streets are congested with hurrying greedy souls; and everywhere are heard the clanking of iron, the rattling of wheels, and whistling of steam. The city has turned into a battlefield where the strong wrestle down the weak and the rich exploit and tyrannize over the poor.

How beautiful is life, my beloved; it is like the poet's heart, filled with light and tenderness.

And how cruel is life, my love, it is like a criminal's heart, throbbing with vice and fear.

Under the Sun

❧

*I have seen all things that are done under the sun,
and behold all is vanity and vexation of spirit.*

ECCLESIASTES

O spirit of Solomon that hovers in the ethereal realm;
you, who cast aside the tattered garment of matter,
have left behind you these words, born of weakness
and misery, which deject those still imprisoned in
bodies.

You know there is a meaning in this life which
Death does not conceal. But how could humanity attain a knowledge which comes only when the soul is
freed from earthly ties?

You realize now that life is not a vexation of spirit;
that things done under the sun are not all vanity; that
somehow everything has ever marched and shall ever
march toward Truth. We miserable creatures have ad-
hered to your earthly sayings as words of great wisdom. But they are shutters that darken the mind and
obliterate hope.

You now understand that ignorance, evil, and des-

potism have their causes; and that Beauty is the revelation of wisdom, the product of virtue and the fruit
of justice.

You now know that sorrow and poverty purify
man's heart; though our weak minds see nothing
worthy in the universe save ease and happiness.

You can see now that the spirit advances toward
the light in spite of worldly hardships. Yet we repeat
your words which teach that a man is but a toy in the
hands of the unknown.

You have regretted your planting in our hearts a
faintness toward life in the world and apprehension
toward life in the hereafter. Yet we persist in heeding
your earthly words.

O spirit of Solomon who now dwells in Eternity,
reveal yourself to the lovers of wisdom and teach them
not to walk the path of heresy and misery. Perchance
this shall be an atonement for an unintended error.

A Glance at the Future

❧

From behind the wall of the Present I heard the hymns of humanity. I heard the sounds of the bells announcing the beginning of the prayer in the temple of Beauty. Bells moulded in the metal of emotion and poised above the holy altar—the human heart.

From behind the Future I saw multitudes worshipping on the bosom of Nature, their faces turned toward the East and awaiting the inundation of the morning light—the morning of Truth.

I saw the city in ruins and nothing remaining to tell man of the defeat of Ignorance and the triumph of Light.

I saw the elders seated under the shade of cypress and willow trees, surrounded by youths listening to their tales of former times.

I saw the youths strumming their guitars and piping on their reeds and the loose-tressed damsels dancing under the jasmine trees.

I saw the husbandmen harvesting the wheat, and the wives gathering the sheaves and singing mirthful songs.

I saw woman adorning herself with a crown of lilies and a girdle of green leaves.

I saw Friendship strengthened between man and all creatures, and clans of birds and butterflies, confident and secure, winging toward the brooks.

I saw no poverty; neither did I encounter excess. I saw fraternity and equality prevailing among man.

I saw not one physician, for everyone had the means and knowledge to heal himself.

I found no priest, for conscience had become the High Priest. Neither did I see a lawyer, for Nature has taken the place of the courts, and treaties of amity and companionship were in force.

I saw that man knew that he is the cornerstone of creation, and that he has raised himself above littleness and baseness and cast off the veil of confusion from the eyes of the soul; this soul now reads what the clouds write on the face of heaven and what the breeze draws on the surface of the water; now understands the meaning of the flower's breath and the cadences of the nightingale.

From behind the wall of the Present, upon the stage of coming ages, I saw Beauty as a groom and Spirit as a bride, and Life as the ceremonial Night of the Kedre.*

---

* A night during the Moslem Lent when God is said to grant the wishes of the devout.

The Goddess of Fantasy

❧

And after a wearying journey I reached the ruins of Palmyra. There I dropped, exhausted, upon the grass that grew among columns shattered and leveled by the ages. They looked like the debris left by invading armies.

At nightfall, as the black mantle of silence enfolded all creatures, I savored a strange scent in the air. It was as fragrant as incense and as inebriating as wine. My spirit opened her mouth to sip the ethereal nectar. Then a hidden hand seemed to press upon my senses and my eyelids grew heavy, while my spirit felt freed of its shackles.

Then the earth swayed under me and the sky trembled over me; whereupon I leaped up as though raised by a magic power. And I found myself in a meadow the like of which no human being has ever fancied. I found myself in the midst of a host of virgins who wore no other raiment than the beauty God gave them. They walked around me, but their feet touched not the grass. They chanted hymns expressing dreams of love. Each maiden played on a lute framed with ivory and strung with gold.

I came upon a vast clearing in the center of which stood a throne inlaid with precious stones and illuminated with the rays of the rainbow. The virgins stood at both sides, raised their voices and faced the direction whence came the scent of myrrh and frankincense. The trees were in bloom and from between the branches, laden with blossoms, a queen walked majestically to the throne. As she seated herself, a flock of doves, white as snow, descended and settled around her feet and formed a crescent, while the maidens chanted hymns of glory. I stood there watching what no man's eyes had seen, and hearing what no man's ears had heard.

Then the Queen motioned, and silence fell. And in a voice that caused my spirit to quiver like the strings of the lute under a player's fingers, she said, "I have called you, man, for I am the Goddess of Fantasy. I have bestowed upon you the honor of standing before me, the Queen of the prairies of dreams. Listen to my commandments, for I appoint you to preach them to the whole human race: explain to man that the city of dreams is a wedding feast at whose door a mighty giant stands on guard. No one may enter unless he wears a wedding garment. Let it be known that this city is a paradise whose sentinel is the angel of Love, and no human may glance at it save he on whose forehead the sign of Love is inscribed. Picture to them these beautiful fields whose streams flow with nectar and wine, whose birds sail in the skies and sing with the angels. Describe the aromatic scent of its flowers and let it be known that only the Son of Dream may tread its soft grass.

"Say that I gave man a cupful of joy; but he, in his ignorance, poured it out. Then the angels of Darkness filled the cup with the brew of Sorrow which he drank and became inebriated.

"Say that none can play the lyre of Life unless his fingers have been blessed by my touch and his eyes sanctified by the sight of my throne.

"Isaiah composed words of wisdom as a necklace of precious stones mounted on the golden chain of my love. Saint John recounted his vision in my behalf. And Dante could not explore the haven of souls save by my guidance. I am metaphor embracing reality, and reality revealing the singleness of the spirit; and a witness confirming the deeds of the gods.

"Truly I say to you that thoughts have a higher dwelling place than the visible world, and its skies are not clouded by sensuality. Imagination finds a road to the realm of the gods, and there man can glimpse that which is to be after the soul's liberation from the world of substance."

And the Goddess of Fantasy drew me toward her with her magic glance and imprinted a kiss upon my burning lips and said, "Tell them that he who passes not his days in the realm of dreams is the slave of the days."

Thereupon the voices of the virgins rose again and the column of incense ascended. Then the earth began to sway again and the sky to tremble; and suddenly I found myself again among Palmyra's sorrowful ruins.

The smiling Dawn had already made its appearance, and between my tongue and my lips were these words: "He who passes not his days in the realm of dreams is the slave of the days."

History and the Nation

❦

By the side of a rivulet that meandered among the rocks at the foot of Lebanon's Mountain sat a shepherdess surrounded by her flock of lean sheep grazing upon dry grass. She looked into the distant twilight as if the future were passing before her. Tears had jewelled her eyes like dew-drops adorning flowers. Sorrow had caused her lips to open that it might enter and occupy her sighing heart.

After sunset, as the knolls and hills wrapped themselves in shadow, History stood before the maiden. He was an old man whose white hair fell like snow over his breast and shoulders, and in his right hand he held a sharp sickle. In a voice like the roaring sea he said, "Peace unto you, Syria."*

The virgin rose, trembling with fear. "What do you wish of me, History?" she asked. Then she pointed to her sheep. "This is the remnant of a healthy flock that once filled this valley. This is all that your covetous-

---

*At the writing of this story Lebanon and Syria were one country known as Syria.

ness has left me. Have you come now to sate your greed on that?

"These plains that were once so fertile have been trodden to barren dust by your trampling feet. My cattle that once grazed upon flowers and produced rich milk, now gnaw thistles that leave them gaunt and dry.

"Fear God, oh History, and afflict me no more. The sight of you has made me detest life, and the cruelty of your sickle has caused me to love Death.

"Leave me in my solitude to drain the cup of sorrow—my best wine. Go, History, to the West where Life's wedding feast is being celebrated. Here let me lament the bereavement you have prepared for me."

Concealing his sickle under the folds of his garment, History looked upon her as a loving father looks upon his child, and said, "Oh Syria, what I have taken from you were my own gifts. Know that your sisternations are entitled to a part of the glory which was yours. I must give to them what I gave you. Your plight is like that of Egypt, Persia, and Greece, for each one of them also has a lean flock and dry pasture. Oh Syria, that which you call degradation is an indispensable sleep from which you will draw strength. The flower does not return to life save through death, and love does not grow except after separation."

The old man came close to the maiden, stretched forth his hand and said, "Shake my hand, oh Daughter of the Prophets." And she shook his hand and looked at him from behind a screen of tears and said, "Fare-well, History, farewell." And he responded, "Until we meet again, Syria, until we meet again."

And the old man disappeared like swift lightning, and the shepherdess called her sheep and started on her way, saying to herself, *"Shall there be another meeting?"*

The Speechless Animal

❦

In the glance of the speechless animal there is a discourse that only the soul of the wise can really understand.

AN INDIAN POET

In the twilight of a beautiful day, when fancy seized upon my mind, I passed by the edge of the city and tarried before the wreck of an abandoned house of which only rubble was left.

In the rubble I saw a dog lying upon dirt and ashes. Sores covered his skin, and sickness racked his feeble body. Staring now and then at the setting sun, his sorrowful eyes expressed humiliation, despair, and misery.

I walked slowly toward him wishing that I knew animal speech so that I might console him with my sympathy. But my approach only terrified him, and he tried to rise on his palsied legs. Falling, he turned a look on me in which helpless wrath was mingled with supplication. In that glance was speech more lucid than man's and more moving than a woman's tears. This is what I understood him to say:

"Man, I have suffered through illness caused by your brutality and persecution.

"I have run from your bruising foot and taken refuge here, for dust and ashes are gentler than man's heart, these ruins less melancholy than the soul of man. Begone, you intruder from the world of misrule and injustice.

"I am a miserable creature who served the son of Adam with faith and loyalty. I was man's faithful companion, I guarded him day and night. I grieved during his absence and welcomed him with joy upon his return. I was contented with the crumbs that fell from his board, and happy with the bones that his teeth had stripped. But when I grew old and ill, he drove me from his home and left me to merciless boys of the alleys.

"Oh son of Adam, I see the similarity between me and your fellow men when age disables them. There are soldiers who fought for their country when they were in the prime of life, and who later tilled its soil. But now that the winter of their life has come and they are useful no longer, they are cast aside.

"I also see a resemblance between my lot and that of a woman who, during the days of her lovely maidenhood enlivened the heart of a young man; and who then, as a mother, devoted her life to her children. But now, grown old, she is ignored and avoided. How oppressive you are, son of Adam, and how cruel!"

Thus spoke the speechless animal whom my heart had understood.

Poets and Poems

❧

If my fellow poets had imagined that the necklaces of verses they composed, and the stanzas whose meters they had strengthened and joined together, would some day become reins to hold back talent, they would have torn up their manuscripts.

If Al-Mutanabbi,* the prophet, had prophesied, and Al-Farid,† the seer, had foreseen that what they had written would become a source for the barren and a forced guide to our poets of today, they would have poured out their inks in the wells of Oblivion, and broken their quills with the hands of Negligence.

If the spirits of Homer, Virgil, Al-Maary,‡ and Milton had known that poetry would become a lapdog of the rich, they would have foresaken a world in which this could occur.

I grieve to hear the language of the spirits prattled

---

* The word Al-Mutanabbi means the one who divines or predicts. He was a famous Arabian poet whose poems were translated into several languages.

† An outstanding Arabian poet and philosopher.

‡ A ninth century Arabian poet who became blind at the age of four and was looked upon as a genius.

by the tongues of the ignorant. It slays my soul to see the wine of the muses flow over the pens of the pretenders.

Neither am I found alone in the vale of Resentment. Say that I am one of the many who see the frog puffed up to imitate the buffalo.

Poetry, my dear friends, is a sacred incarnation of a smile. Poetry is a sigh that dries the tears. Poetry is a spirit who dwells in the soul, whose nourishment is the heart, whose wine is affection. Poetry that comes not in this form is a false messiah.

Oh spirits of the poets, who watch over us from the heaven of Eternity, we go to the altars you have adorned with the pearls of your thoughts and the gems of your souls because we are oppressed by the clang of steel and the clamor of factories. Therefore our poems are as heavy as freight trains and as annoying as steam whistles.

And you, the real poets, forgive us. We belong in the New World where men run after worldly goods; and poetry, too, is a commodity today, and not a breath of immortality.

Among the Ruins

❧

The moon dropped its gauzy veil over the gardens of the City of the Sun,* and silence swathed all beings. The fallen palaces looked menacing, like sneering monsters.

At that hour two phantoms, like vapor rising from the blue water of a lake, sat on a marble pillar pondering the scene which was like a realm of magic. One lifted his head, and with a voice that set echoes reverberating, said:

"These are the remnants of temples I built for you, my beloved, and this is the rubble of a palace I erected for your enjoyment. Nothing else remains to tell the nations of the glory to which I devoted my life, and of the pomp for which I exploited the weak.

"Think and ponder, my beloved, upon the elements that triumphed over my city, and upon Time that thus belittled my efforts.

"Oblivion has submerged the empire I established, and naught is left save atoms of love which your

---

* The ruined City of Baalbek.

74

beauty has created, and effects of beauty which your love has enlivened.

"I erected a temple in Jerusalem and the priests sanctified it, but time has destroyed it. But in my heart the altar I built for Love was consecrated by God and sustained against the powers of destruction.

"Men said of me, 'What a wise king he is!' The angels said, 'How trifling is his wisdom.' But the angels rejoiced when I found you, my beloved, and sang for you the song of Love and longing; though men heard no notes of my hymn. . . .

"The days of my reign were barriers to my understanding of Love and of the beauty of life, but when I saw you, Love awoke and demolished those barriers, and I lamented the life I spent considering everything under the sun as vanity.

"As Love enlightened me, I became humble both before the tribes who had feared my military might and before my own people.

"But when death came, it buried my deadly weapons in earth and carried my love to God."

And the other phantom said, "As the flower obtains life and aromatic scent from earth, so the soul extracts wisdom and strength from the weakness and errors of matter."

Then the two fused into one and walked away, saying:

"Eternity keeps naught but Love,
For Love is like Eternity."

At the Door of the Temple

❧

I purified my lips with the sacred fire, to speak of Love, but could find no words.

When Love became known to me, the words lapsed into a faint gasping, and the song in my heart into deep silence.

Oh you who asked me about Love, whom I convinced of its mysteries and wonders, now since Love has wrapped me in its veil, I come to ask you about Love's course and merit.

Who can answer my questions? I ask about that which is in me; I seek to be informed about myself.

Who among you can reveal my inner self to myself and my soul to my soul?

Tell me, for Love's sake, what is that flame which burns in my heart and devours my strength and dissolves my will?

What are those hidden soft and rough hands that grasp my soul; what is that wine mixed of bitter joy and sweet pain that suffuses my heart?

What are those wings that hover over my pillow in

the silence of Night, and keep me awake, watching no one knows what?

What is the invisible thing I stare at, the incomprehensible thing that I ponder, the feeling that cannot be sensed?

In my sighs is a grief more beautiful than the echo of laughter and more rapturous than joy.

Why do I surrender myself to an unknown power that slays me and revives me until Dawn rises and fills my chamber with its light?

Phantoms of wakefulness tremble between my seared eyelids, and shadows of dreams hover over my stony bed.

What is that which we call Love? Tell me, what is that secret hidden within the ages yet which permeates all consciousness?

What is this consciousness that is at once origin and result of everything?

What is this vigil that fashions from Life and Death a dream, stranger than Life and deeper than Death?

Tell me, friends, is there one among you who would not awake from the slumber of Life if Love touched his soul with its fingertip?

Which one of you would not leave his father and mother at the call of the virgin whom his heart loves?

Who among you would not sail the distant seas, cross the deserts, and climb the topmost peak to meet the woman whom his soul has chosen?

What youth's heart would not follow to the ends of

the world the maiden whose aromatic breath, sweet voice, and magic-soft hands have enraptured his soul?

What being would not burn his heart as incense before a god who listens to his supplications and grants his prayer?

Yesterday I stood at the temple door interrogating the passers-by about the mystery and merit of Love.

And before me passed an old man with an emaciated and melancholy face, who sighed and said:

"Love is a natural weakness bestowed upon us by the first man."

But a virile youth retorted:

"Love joins our present with the past and the future."

Then a woman with a tragic face sighed and said:

"Love is a deadly poison injected by black vipers, that crawl from the caves of hell. The poison seems fresh as dew and the thirsty soul eagerly drinks it; but after the first intoxication the drinker sickens and dies a slow death."

Then a beautiful, rosy-cheeked damsel smilingly said:

"Love is wine served by the brides of Dawn which strengthens strong souls and enables them to ascend to the stars."

After her a black-robed, bearded man, frowning, said:

"Love is the blind ignorance with which youth begins and ends."

Another, smiling, declared:

"Love is a divine knowledge that enables men to see as much as the gods."

Then said a blind man, feeling his way with a cane:

"Love is a blinding mist that keeps the soul from discerning the secret of existence, so that the heart sees only trembling phantoms of desire among the hills, and hears only echoes of cries from voiceless valleys."

A young man, playing on his viol, sang:

"Love is a magic ray emitted from the burning core of the soul and illuminating the surrounding earth. It enables us to perceive Life as a beautiful dream between one awakening and another."

And a feeble ancient, dragging his feet like two rags, said, in quavering tones:

"Love is the rest of the body in the quiet of the grave, the tranquility of the soul in the depth of Eternity."

And a five-year-old child, after him, said laughing:

"Love is my father and mother, and no one knows Love save my father and mother."

And so, all who passed spoke of Love as the image of their hopes and frustrations, leaving it a mystery as before.

Then I heard a voice within the temple:

"Life is divided into two halves, one frozen, the other aflame; the burning half is Love."

Thereupon I entered the temple, kneeling, rejoicing, and praying:

> "Make me, O Lord, nourishment
> for the blazing flame . . .
> Make me, O God, food for the
> sacred fire . . . Amen."

Narcotics and Dissecting Knives

"He is excessive and fanatic to the point of madness. Though he is an idealist, his literary aim is to poison the mind of the youths. . . . If men and women were to follow Gibran's counsels on marriage, family ties would break, society would perish, and the world would become an inferno peopled by demons and devils.

"His style is seductively beautiful, magnifying the danger of this inveterate enemy of mankind. Our counsel to the inhabitants of this blessed Mountain (Mount Lebanon) is to reject the insidious teachings of this anarchist and heretic and to burn his books, that his doctrines may not lead the innocent astray. We have read *The Broken Wings* and found it to be honeyed poison."

Such is what people say of me and they are right, for I am indeed a fanatic and I am inclined toward destruction as well as construction. There is hatred in my heart for that which my detractors sanctify, and love for that which they reject. And if I could uproot certain customs, beliefs, and traditions of the people, I would do so without hesitation. When they said my books were poison, they were speaking truth about themselves, for what I say is poison to them. But they falsified when they said I mix honey into it, for I apply the poison full strength and pour it from transparent glass. Those who call me an idealist becalmed in clouds are the very ones who turn away from the transparent glass they call poison, knowing that their stomachs cannot digest it.

This may sound truculent, but is not truculence preferable to seductive pretense?

The people of the Orient demand that the writer be like a bee always making honey. They are gluttonous for honey and prefer it to all other food.

The people of the Orient want their poet to burn himself as incense before their sultans. The Eastern skies have become sickly with incense yet the people of the Orient have not had enough.

They ask the world to learn their history, to study their antiquities, customs and traditions, and acquire their languages. They also expect those who know them not to repeat the words of Baidaba the Philosopher, Ben Rished, Ephraim Al-Syriani, and John of Damascus.

In brief, the people of the Orient seek to make their past a justification and a bed of ease. They shun positive thinking and positive teachings and any knowledge of reality that might sting them and awake them from their slumber.

The Orient is ill, but it has become so inured to its infirmities that it has come to see them as natural and even noble qualities that distinguish them above others. They consider one who lacks such qualities as incomplete and unfit for the divine gift of perfection.

Numerous are the social healers in the Orient, and many are their patients who remain uncured but appear eased of their ills because they are under the effects of social narcotics. But these tranquilizers merely mask the symptoms.

Such narcotics are distilled from many sources but the chief is the Oriental philosophy of submission to Destiny (the act of God). Another source is the cowardice of the social physicians who fear to aggravate pain by administration of drastic medicine.

Here are some samples of these social tranquilizers:

A husband and wife, for substantial reasons, find that hate has replaced love between them. After long mutual torment they separate. Immediately their parents meet and work out some agreement for the reconciliation of the estranged couple. First they ply the wife with falsehoods, then they work on the husband with similar deceits. Neither is convinced, but they are shamed into a pretense of peace. This cannot endure; soon the effects of the social narcotics have worn off, and the miserable pair return for further doses.

Or a group or party revolts against a despotic government and advocates political reforms to free the oppressed from their shackles. They distribute manifestoes and deliver fiery speeches and publish stinging articles. But a month later, we hear that the government has either imprisoned the leader or silenced him by giving him an important position. And nothing more is heard.

Or a sect rebels against its religious leader, accusing him of misdeeds and threatening to adopt another religion, more humane and free of superstition. But shortly we hear that the wise men of the country have reconciled the shepherd and the flock, through the application of social narcotics.

When a weak man complains of oppression by a strong, his neighbor will quieten him, "Hush, the eye of the stubborn seer cannot withstand the blow of the spear."

When a villager doubts the holiness of the priest, he will be told, "Listen only to his teaching and disregard his shortcomings and misdeeds."

When a teacher rebukes a student, he will say, "The excuses that a lazy youth invents are often worse than the crime."

If a daughter refuses to adhere to her mother's customs, the mother will say, "The daughter is not better than the mother; she should follow in her mother's footsteps."

Should a young man ask a priest to enlighten him

about an ancient rite, the preacher will reprove him, "Son, he who does not look at religion with the eyes of Faith, will see nothing save mist and smoke."

Thus the Orient lies upon its soft bed. The sleeper wakes for an instant when stung by a flea, and then resumes his narcotic slumber.

Whoever tries to awaken him is berated as a rude person who neither sleeps himself nor lets others sleep. Shutting their eyes again, they whisper into the ears of their souls, "He is an infidel poisoning the mind of the youths and undermining the foundation of the ages."

Many times I have asked my soul, "Am I one of those awakened rebels who reject narcotics?" And my soul answered with cryptic words. But hearing my name and principles reviled, I was assured that I was awake and could count myself among those who do not surrender themselves to pipe dreams, that I belong with the stronghearted who walk narrow and thorny paths where flowers are also to be found, amidst howling wolves—and singing nightingales.

If awakening were a virtue, modesty would prevent me from claiming it. But it is not a virtue, but a reality that appears suddenly to those who have the strength to rise. To be modest in speaking truth is hypocrisy. Alas that the people of the Orient call it education.

I will not be surprised if the "thinkers" say of me, "He is a man of excess who looks upon life's seamy side and reports nothing but gloom and lamentation."

To them I declare, "I deplore our Oriental urge to evade the reality of weakness and sorrow.

"I grieve that my beloved country sings, not in joy, but to still the quakings of fear.

"In battling evil, excess is good; for he who is moderate in announcing the truth is presenting half-truth. He conceals the other half out of fear of the people's wrath.

"I loathe the carrion mind; its stench upsets my stomach. I will not serve it with sweets and cordials.

"Yet I will gladly exchange my outcries for cheerful laughter, speak eulogies instead of indictments, replace excess with moderation, provided you show me a just governor, a lawyer of integrity, a religious hierarch who practices what he preaches, a husband who looks upon his wife with the same eyes as he looks upon himself.

"If you prefer me to dance, to blow the trumpet or beat the drum, invite me to a wedding feast and lead me out of the graveyard."

The Giants

We live in an era whose humblest men are becoming greater than the greatest men of preceding ages. What once preoccupied our minds is now of no consequence. The veil of indifference covers it. The beautiful dreams that once hovered in our consciousness have been dispersed like mist. In their place are giants moving like tempests, raging like seas, breathing like volcanoes.

What destiny will the giants bring the world at the end of their struggles?

Will the farmer return to his field to sow where Death has planted the bones of the dead?

Will the shepherd pasture his flock on fields mown by the sword?

Will the sheep drink from springs whose waters are stained with blood?

Will the worshipper kneel in a profaned temple at whose altars Satanists have danced?

Will the poet compose his songs under stars veiled in gun smoke?

Will the musician strum his lute in a night whose silence was ravished by terror?

Will the mother at the cradle of her infant, brooding on the perils of tomorrow, be able to sing a lullaby?

Can lovers meet and exchange kisses on battlefields still acrid with bomb fumes?

Will Nisan* ever return to earth and dress the earth's wounds with its garment?

What will be the destiny of your country and mine? Which giant shall seize the mountains and valleys that produced us and reared us and made us men and women before the face of the sun?

Will Syria remain lying between the wolf lair and the pigsty? Or will it move with the tempest to the lion's den or soar to the eagle's eyrie?

Will the dawn of a new Time ever appear over Lebanon's peaks?

Every time I am alone I ask my soul these questions. But my soul is mute like Destiny.

Which one of you, people, does not ponder day and night on the fate of the world under the rule of the giants intoxicated with the tears of widows and orphans?

I am among those who believe in the Law of Evolution; I believe that ideal entities evolve, like brute beings, and that religions and governments are raised to higher planes.

The law of evolution has a severe and oppressive countenance and those of limited or fearful mind

---

* The month of April.

dread it; but its principles are just, and those who study them become enlightened. Through its Reason men are raised above themselves and can approach the sublime.

All around me are dwarves who see the giants emerging; and the dwarves croak like frogs:

"The world has returned to savagery. What science and education have created is being destroyed by the new primitives. We are now like the prehistoric cave dwellers. Nothing distinguishes us from them save our machines of destruction and our improved techniques of slaughter."

Thus speak those who measure the world's conscience by their own. They measure the range of all Existence by the tiny span of their individual being. As if the sun did not exist but for their warmth, as if the sea was created for them to wash their feet.

From the heart of life, from deep within the universe where the secrets of Creation are stored, the giants rise like winds and ascend like clouds, and convene like mountains. In their struggles age-old problems are being brought to solution.

But man, in spite of all his knowledge and skills, and notwithstanding the love and hatred in his heart, and the torments he endures, is but a tool in the hands of the giants, to reach their goal and accomplish their inevitable high purpose.

The streams of blood shall some day become flow-ing rivers of wine; and the tears that bedewed the earth shall bring forth aromatic flowers; and the souls that left their abodes shall assemble and appear from behind the new horizon as a new Morn. Then man will realize that he had bought Justice and Reason in the slave market. He will understand that he who works and spends for the sake of Right will never lose.

Nisan shall come, but he who seeks Nisan without Winter's aid, will never find it.

Out of Earth

Wrathfully and violently earth comes out of earth;
and gracefully and majestically earth walks over
earth.
Earth from earth, builds palaces and erects towers
and temples,
And earth weaves on earth, legends, doctrines, and
laws.

Then earth becomes tired of the deeds of earth and
wreathes from its halo, dreams and fantasies.

And earth's eyes are then beguiled by earth's slumber
to enduring rest.
And earth calls unto earth:
"I am the womb and the sepulchre, and I shall
remain a womb and a sepulchre until the planets
exist no more and the sun turns into ashes."

O Night

𑁍

O Night of lovers, inspirer of poets and singers,
O Night of phantoms, of spirits and fancies,
O Night of longing, of hopes and memories,
You are like a giant dwarfing the evening clouds
 and towering over the dawn.
With the sword of fear you are armed, and with
 the shining moon you are crowned, and with calm
 and silence you are veiled.

With a thousand eyes you penetrate the depth
 of life,
With a thousand ears you hear the moan
 of death and non-existence.
The light of heaven shines through your darkness,
For Day is but light overwhelming us with the
 obscurity of the earth.
Before the awe of eternity you open our eyes and
 give us hope,
For Day is a deceiver that blinds us
 with measures and quantities.

You are perfect silence revealing the secrets of
    the awakened spirits in heaven,
But day is an uproar agitating the souls that
    lie between the hooves of purpose and wonder.
You are Justice that brings unto the haven of
    slumber the dreams of the weak, that they may
    be united with the hopes of the strong.

You are a merciful monarch who closes with his
    fingers of enchantment the eyes of the miserable,
    and conveys their hearts into a gentler realm.

The lovers' spirits find refuge between the folds of
    your blue garment,
And upon your feet, drenched with dew, the
    forlorn shed their tears.

In the palms of your hands, where lies the fragrance
    of the valleys, strangers find ease for their
    yearnings.

You are the companion of lovers; you console the
    desolate; you shelter the alien and the lonely.
In your shadow the poet's affections rest, and
    the hearts of the prophets awaken,
And under your crown the
    wisdom of the thinker takes form.
You inspire poets; you bring revelation to the
    prophets; you instruct the philosophers.

When my soul wearies of humanity, when my
    eyes tire of staring into the face of the day,
I wander where the phantoms
    of past ages sleep.

There I pause before a dim presence who strode
    with a thousand feet over the earth, setting it
    atremble.

There I look into the eyes of shadow, and
    listen to the rustle of invisible wings, and feel
    the soft touch of the unseen garment of silence,
    and withstand the terrors of black darkness.

There I see you, Night, awful and beautiful,
    poised between heaven and earth, veiled in
    mist, cloaked in cloud, laughing at
    the sun, ridiculing the day, taunting the slaves
    who sleeplessly worship before the idols.

I see your wrath against kings sleeping upon beds of
    velvet and silk;
I see thieves flinching before your vigilant gaze as
    you guard the babes in slumber;
I see you weeping over the forced smiles of prostitutes
    and smiling over tears of true lovers;
I see your right hand raising up the good and your
    feet trampling the wicked.

There, I see you and you see me, Night. And though
 terrible, you are like a father to me, and I,
 dreaming, envision myself as your son.

The screen of distrust has been removed
 from between us, and you reveal to me
 your secrets and designs.
And I disclose to you my hopes and my desires.
Your terrors have turned into a melody sweeter and
 more soothing to the heart than the whisper of
 the flowers.

My fears are vanished and I am more tranquil
 than birds.
You have lifted me unto you and held me between
 your arms and taught my eyes to see, and my ears
 to hear, and my lips to speak, and my heart to
 love that which others hate, and to hate that
 which others love.
You touch my thoughts with your
 gentle fingers, and my contemplation flows like
 a strong stream.

With your burning lips you print a kiss
 upon the lips of my soul
 and set it aflame like a torch.

I have accompanied you, O Night, and followed you
 until we became akin.

I loved you until my being became a diminutive image
of your being.

In my dark self are glittering stars strewn
by my emotions.
And in my heart shines a moon lighting the processions
of my dreams.
In my sleepless soul a silence reveals
the lover's secrets and echoes the
worshipper's prayers,
And my face wears a magic mask. Torn by
the agony of death, it is mended by the songs of
youth.
We are both alike in every way, Night.

Will man consider me boastful if I liken myself
unto you?
Does not man boast of his resemblance to the day?
I am like you, Night, and we are both accused of
being what we are not.
I am like you even though twilight does not crown me
with its golden clouds.
I am like you although morn does not adorn the
hem of my garment with its rosy rays.
I am like you though I am not encircled by the milky
way.
I am night boundless and calm; there is no beginning
to my obscurity and no end to my depth.

When the souls rise in the
    light of their joy, my soul ascends glorified by the
    dark of grief.
I am like you, Night! And when my morn comes, then
    my time will end.

Earth

How beautiful you are, Earth, and how sublime!
How perfect is your obedience to the light, and
how noble is your submission to the sun!

How lovely you are, veiled in shadow, and how
charming your face, masked with obscurity!

How soothing is the song of your dawn, and how
harsh are the praises of your eventide!
How perfect you are, Earth, and how majestic!

I have walked over your plains, I have climbed your
stony mountains; I have descended into your
valleys; I have entered into your caves.
In the plains, I found your dream; upon the mountain
I found your pride; in the valley I witnessed your
tranquility; in the rocks your resolution; in the
cave your secrecy.

You are weak and powerful and humble and haughty.
You are pliant and rigid, and clear and secret.
I have ridden your seas and explored your rivers and
     followed your brooks.
I heard Eternity speak through your ebb and flow,
     and the ages echoing your songs among your hills.
I listened to life calling to life in your mountain
     passes and along your slopes.
You are the mouth and lips of Eternity, the strings
     and fingers of Time, the mystery and solution of
     Life.
Your Spring has awakened me and led me to your
     fields where your aromatic breath ascends like
     incense.
I have seen the fruits of your Summer labor.
In Autumn, in your vineyards, I saw your
     blood flow as wine.
Your Winter carried me into your bed, where the snow
     attested your purity.
In your Spring you are an aromatic essence; in your
     Summer you are generous; in your Autumn you
     are a source of plenty.

One calm and clear night I opened the windows and
     doors of my soul and went out to see you, my
     heart tense with lust and greed.
And I saw you staring at the stars that smiled at
     you. So I cast away my fetters, for I

found out that the dwelling place of the soul is in
your space.
Its desires grow in your desires; its peace rests in
your peace; and its happiness is in the golden
dust which the stars sprinkle upon your body.

One night, as the skies turned gray, and my soul was
wearied and anxious, I went out to you.
And you appeared to me like a giant, armed with
raging tempests, fighting the past with the present,
replacing the old with the new, and letting the
strong disperse the weak.

Whereupon I learned that the law of the people is
your law.
I learned that he who does not break his dry branches
with his tempest, will die wearily,
And he who does not use revolution, to strip
his dry leaves, will slowly perish.

How generous you are, Earth, and how strong is your
yearning for your children lost between that
which they have attained and that which they
could not obtain.
We clamor and you smile; we flit
but you stay!
We blaspheme and you consecrate.
We defile and you sanctify.

We sleep without dreams; but you
    dream in your eternal wakefulness.

We pierce your bosom with swords and spears,
And you dress our wounds with oil and balsam.
We plant your fields with skulls and bones,
    and from them you rear cypress
    and willow trees.

We empty our wastes in your bosom, and you fill
    our threshing-floors with wheat sheaves, and
    our winepresses with grapes.

We extract your elements to make cannons and
    bombs, but out of our elements you create
    lilies and roses.

How patient you are, Earth, and how merciful!
Are you an atom of dust raised by
    the feet of God when He journeyed from the east
    to the west of the Universe?
Or a spark projected from the furnace
    of Eternity?
Are you a seed dropped in the field of the
    firmament to become God's tree reaching above
    the heavens with its celestial branches?
Or are you a drop of blood in the veins of the
    giant of giants, or a bead of sweat upon his
    brow?

Are you a fruit ripened by the sun?
Do you grow from the tree of Absolute
    Knowledge, whose roots extend through
    Eternity, and whose branches soar through
    the Infinite?

Are you a jewel placed by the God of Time in the
    palm of the God of Space?

Who are you, Earth, and what are you?
You are "I," Earth!

You are my sight and my discernment.
You are my knowledge and my
    dream.
You are my hunger and my thirst.
You are my sorrow and my joy.
You are my inadvertence and my wakefulness.
You are the beauty that lives in my eyes,
    the longing in my heart, the everlasting life
    in my soul.

You are "I," Earth.
Had it not been for my being,
    You would not have been.

Perfection

❦

You ask me, my brother, when will man reach
    perfection. Hear my answer:
Man approaches perfection when he
    feels that he is an infinite space and a sea
    without a shore,
An everlasting fire, an unquenchable
    light,
A calm wind or a raging tempest, a thunder-
    ing sky or a rainy heaven,
A singing brook or a wailing rivulet, a tree abloom
    in Spring, or a naked sapling
    in Autumn,
A rising mountain or a descending valley,
A fertile plain or a desert.

When man feels all these, he has already
    reached halfway to perfection. To attain his goal
    he must then perceive
    that he is a child dependent upon his mother,
    a father responsible for his family,

A youth lost in love,

An ancient wrestling against his past,

A worshipper in his temple, a criminal in
    his prison,

A scholar amidst his parchments,

An ignorant soul stumbling between the darkness of
    his night and the obscurity of his day,

A nun suffering between the flowers of her faith and
    the thistles of her loneliness,

A prostitute caught between the fangs of her
    weakness and the claws of her needs,

A poor man trapped between his bitterness and his
    submission,

A rich man between his greed and his conscience,

A poet between the mist of his twilight and the
    rays of his dawn.

Who can experience, see, and understand
    these things can reach perfection and
    become a shadow of God's Shadow.

Yesterday, Today, and Tomorrow

I said to my friend,

    "See her leaning over his arm?

    Yesterday she leaned over my arm."

And he said:

    "Tomorrow she will lean over mine."

And I said,

    "See her sitting at his side;

    And yesterday she sat at my side."

And he said:

    "Tomorrow she will sit at mine."

And I said,

    "Don't you see her drinking from his

    Cup?

    And yesterday she sipped from mine."

And he said:

    "Tomorrow she will drink from mine."

And I said,

    "Look how she glances at him with eyes

    full of love!

And with just such love, yesterday
she glanced at me."

And he said:

"Tomorrow she will glance at me
likewise."

And I said,

"Listen to her whispering songs of
love in his ear.
And yesterday she whispered the same songs
in mine."

And he said:

"Tomorrow she will whisper them
in mine."

And I said,

"Look at her embracing him; and yesterday she embraced me."

And he said:

"Tomorrow she will lie in my arms."

And I said,

"What a strange woman she is!!"

And he said:

"She is Life."

A Story of a Friend

❧

I

I knew him as a youth lost on the paths of life, goaded by wild impulse and following death in pursuit of his desires. I knew him as a tender flower borne by the winds of rashness into the sea of lust.

I knew him in that village as an ill-natured boy tearing with cruel hands at the birds' nests and slaying the nestlings and trampling with his feet the beautiful crowns of the sweet flowers.

I knew him at school as an adolescent averse to learning, arrogant, and an enemy of peace.

I knew him in the city as a young man trading his father's honor in sinister markets, spending his father's money in houses of ill-fame, and surrendering his mind to the fruit of the vine.

However, I loved him. And my love for him was a mingling of sorrow and sympathy. I loved him because his sins were not born of a small spirit, but rather the deeds of a lost and desperate soul.

The spirit, my dear people, strays from the path of wisdom unwillingly, but returns to it willingly. When the whirlwinds of youth blow dust and sand, the eyes are blind for a time.

I loved that youth because I saw the dove of his conscience struggling with the hawk of his evils. And I saw that the dove was subdued not by its own cowardice but by the strength of its enemy.

Conscience is a just but a weak judge. Weakness leaves it powerless to execute its judgment.

I said I loved him. And love comes in different shapes. Sometimes it comes in wisdom; at other times in justice; and oftentimes in hope. My love for him sustained my hope of seeing the light in him triumph over the darkness. But I knew not when and where would his defilement turn into purity, his brutality into meekness, his recklessness into wisdom. Man does not know in what manner the soul frees itself from the slavery of matter until after it is freed. Neither does man know how the flowers smile save after the coming of the morn.

II

The days passed, following the nights, and I remembered the youth with painful sighs; I repeated his name with affection that made the heart bleed. Then yesterday a letter came from him saying:

"Come to me, my friend, for I wish to unite you with a young man whom your heart will rejoice to meet, and your soul will be refreshed to know."

I said, "Woe is me! Does he intend to mingle his sad friendship with another one similar to it? Is he not alone a sufficient example to the world of error and sin? Does he now wish to re-enforce his misdeeds with those of his companion so that I may see them in double darkness?"

Then I said to myself, "I must go; perhaps the wise soul shall reap figs from the brambles, and the loving heart shall extract light from the darkness."

When night came I found him alone in his room reading a book of verses. "Where is the new friend?" I said, and he answered, "I am he, my friend." And he displayed a calmness I had never seen in him before. In his eyes I could now see a strange light that penetrated the heart. Those eyes in which I had seen cruelty before, were radiant with the light of kindness. Then with a voice that I thought came from another, he said, "The youth whom you knew during childhood and with whom you walked to school, is dead. With his death I was born. I am your new friend; take my hand."

As I shook his hand I felt the existence of a gentle spirit circulating with the blood. His iron hand had become soft and kind. His fingers which yesterday tore like a tiger's claws, today caress the heart.

Then I spoke again. "Who are you, and what has happened? How have you become this kind of person? Has the Holy Spirit entered your heart and sanctified your soul? Or are you playing a part, the invention of a poet?"

And he said, "Ay, my friend, the spirit descended upon me and blessed me. A great love has made my heart a pure altar. It is woman, my friend—woman that I thought yesterday a toy in the hands of man— who has delivered me from the darkness of hell and opened before me the gates of Paradise where I have entered. A true woman has taken me into the Jordan River of her love and baptized me. The woman whose sister I disrespected through my ignorance has exalted me to the throne of glory. The woman whose companion I have defiled with my wickedness has purified my heart with her affections. The woman whose kind I have enslaved with my father's gold has freed me with her beauty. The woman who had Adam driven from Paradise by the strength of her will has restored me to Paradise by her tenderness and my obedience."

Ashes of the Ages and Eternal Fire

❧

I

SPRING OF THE YEAR 116 B.C.

Night and silence had fallen over the slumbering City of the Sun.* The lamps were extinguished in the dwellings among the majestic temples standing amid olive and laurel groves. The moon's silver light laved the marble columns that stood like giant sentinels before the houses of the gods.

At that hour, while souls succumbed to slumber, Nathan, son of the High Priest, entered Ishtar's temple, bearing a torch in quaking hands. He lit the lamps and censers and soon the fragrance of myrrh and frankincense rose to the uppermost corners. Then he knelt before the altar, inlaid with ivory and gold, raised his hands toward Ishtar,† and with a choking voice cried out, "Have mercy upon me, O great Ishtar,

---

* Baalbek, or the City of Baal, the sun god of ancient Syria; in Graeco-Roman times its name was changed to Heliopolis, the Greek term for City of the Sun. It was considered the most beautiful city in the ancient Middle East. The ruins are mainly Roman.

† Ishtar, great goddess of the Phoenicians, was worshipped in the cities of Tyre, Sidon, Sur, Djabeil and Baalbek, and there called Burner of the Torch of Life, and Guardian of Youth. She was the counterpart of Aphrodite, the Greek goddess of Love and Beauty, and of the Roman goddess, Venus.

goddess of Love and Beauty. Be merciful and hold back the hands of Death from my beloved, whom my soul has chosen by thy will. The potions of the physicians and spells of the wizards are of no avail. Naught is left save thy holy will. Thou art my guide and my aid. Gaze upon my crushed heart and aching soul with pity and grant my prayer. Spare my beloved's life so that together we may worship thee with the rites of love and devote to you our youth and beauty.

"Your servant Nathan, son of your High Priest Hiram, loves a maiden without peer and has made her his companion. But some female djin envied her loveliness and my passion for her and breathed into her a deadly plague, and now the messenger of Death stands at her bedside, spreading his black-ribbed wings over her, and unsheathing his sharp claws. Have mercy upon us, I beseech thee. Spare that flower which has not yet rejoiced in its summer.*

"Save her from the grasp of Death so that we may sing hymns of praise to thee and burn incense in thine honor and offer sacrifices at thine altar and fill thy vases with perfumed oil and spread roses and violets upon the portico of thy temple. Let Love overcome Death in this struggle of Joy against Sorrow."

And Nathan, exhausted, could say no more.

At that moment his slave entered the temple, has-

---

* During the "Era of Ignorance" the period before the coming of Mohammed), the Arabs believed that if a female genie loved a human youth, she would prevent him from marrying, and if he did wed, she would bewitch the bride and cause her to die. This superstition persists today in isolated villages in Lebanon.

tened to him, and whispered, "Master, she calls for you."

Nathan ran to his palace and entered the chamber of his beloved. He leaned over her bed, held her frail hand, and kissed her lips as if striving to breathe life into her body from his. Slowly she opened her eyes, and upon her lips appeared a faint smile, herald of a last heartbeat. With a feeble voice she said, "The goddess calls me, Oh Life of my Soul. Her servant, Death has come. The will of the goddess is sacred, and the errand of Death is just. I depart now, and I hear the rustle of the whiteness descending. But the cups of Love and Youth remain in our hands, and flowery paths of beautiful Life extend before us. I embark, my Beloved, upon an ark of the spirit, but I shall return to you; for great Ishtar will restore those souls of lovers who have not enjoyed their share of sweet Love and happy Youth."*

Weeping, Nathan bent down to kiss her and found her lips already cold. He cried out and began tearing his raiment, and his lamentations awoke the sleeping. At dawn many came to Nathan's palace to offer their sympathy. But Nathan had disappeared. After a fortnight, the chief of a newly arrived caravan related that he had seen Nathan in the distant wilderness, wandering among a flock of gazelles.

---

* This belief recurs in Asian thought. Mohammed said, "You were dead and He brought you back to life, and He will slay you again and revive you, whereupon you shall return to Him." Buddha said, "Yesterday we existed, and today, and we will return to this life, again and again, until we become perfect like God."

The ages passed. In place of Ishtar, goddess of Love and Beauty, a destroying goddess reigned. She pulled down the magnificent temples of the City of the Sun; she demolished its beautiful palaces. She laid waste the orchards and fields. The land was scarred with ruins.

II

SPRING OF THE YEAR 1890 A.D.

The sun withdrew its golden rays from the plain of Baalbek. Ali El Hosseini* brought his sheep back to the sheds in the ruins of the temples. He sat among the ancient columns and piped to his flock.

Midnight came and heaven sowed the seeds of the following day in the deep furrows of the darkness. Ali's eyes became heavy and sleep captured his senses. He encountered his invisible self, who dwelt in a higher realm and the range of his vision broadened, bringing Life's hidden secrets to his view. His soul stood aside from Time rushing toward nothingness; it stood amid symmetrical thoughts and crystal ideas. For the first time in his life, Ali became aware of the causes of the spiritual hunger of his youth, the longing which neither the glory of the world nor passing time can still. Ali felt the ache of a centuries-old Memory, kindling like incense placed upon white-hot firebrands.

---

* The Hosseinese are an Arabian tribe, living in tents pitched in the plains surrounding the ruins of Baalbek.

A magic love touched his heart as a musician's delicate fingers touch quivering strings.

Ali looked at the ruins and then, like a blind man whose sight is suddenly restored, he recalled the lamps and the silver censers before the shrine of a goddess. . . . He recalled sacrifices at an altar of gold and ivory. . . . He saw again dancing maidens, tambourine players, singers who chanted hymns to the goddess of Love . . . and Beauty. . . . But how could such memories live in the heart of a simple shepherd youth born in a nomad's tent?

Suddenly the memories tore away the veil of oblivion and he rose and walked to the temple. At the cavernous entrance he halted as if a magnetic power had gripped his feet. Looking down, he saw a smashed statue on the ground, and the sight freed his soul's tears and they poured like blood from a deep wound. He also felt a stabbing loneliness and remoteness like an abyss between his heart and the heart from whom he had been torn before he entered upon this life.

"Who are you," Ali cried in anguish, "who stand close to my heart but unseen by my eyes? Are you a phantom from Eternity to show me the vanity of Life and the weakness of mankind? Or the spirit of a genie stolen out of earth's crevices to enslave me and render me an object of mockery? What is your strange power which at one time prostrates and enlivens my heart? Who am I and what is this strange self whom I call 'Myself'? Has the Water of Life which I have drunk made me an angel in communion with the universe and its mysteries? Or is it inebriating wine that blinds me to myself?

"Oh, what the soul reveals, and the night conceals. . . . Oh, beautiful spirit, hovering in the firmament of my dream, disclose yourself to me if you are human or command Slumber to shut my eyes so I can view your divine vastness. If you are human, let me touch you; let me hear your voice. Tear away this veil that conceals you from me. If I am worthy, place your hand upon my heart and possess me."

Thus an hour passed, with Ali shedding tears and voicing his yearnings.

Then Dawn appeared and the morning breeze stirred. The birds left their nests and sang their morning prayers.

Ali placed his cupped hand over his forehead. Like Adam, when God opened his eyes with his all-creating breath, Ali saw new objects, strange and fantastic. He called to his sheep and they followed him quietly toward the meadow. As he led them, he felt like a philosopher with the power to divine the secrets of the Universe. He reached a brook whose murmuring was soothing to his spirit, and sat under a willow tree whose branches dipped over the water as if drinking from the cool depths.

Here Ali felt the beating of his heart increase and through his soul throbbed a strong and almost visible vibration. He sprang up like a mother suddenly awakened from her slumber by the scream of her child, and his eyes were magnetized by the sight of a beautiful maiden approaching from the opposite side, with a water jar on her shoulder. As she leaned over to fill the jar, her eyes and Ali's met. She cried out, distraught, dropped the jar, and ran off, but glanced back in agonizing disbelief.

Ali, compelled by the mysterious power, leaped across the brook, caught the maiden and embraced her. As if this caress had subdued her will she did not move, yielding to him as the fragrance of jasmine submits to the breeze. Both felt it to be the reunion of souls long separated by earth and now brought together by God.

The enamored pair walked amidst the willow trees, and the unity of the two selves was a speaking tongue for them; an eye to see the glory of Happiness; a silent auditor of the tremendous revelation of Love.

The sheep grazed; the birds of the sky hovered above their heads; the sun spread a golden garment upon the hills; and they sat by the side of a rock where the violets hid. The maiden looked into Ali's black eyes while the breeze caressed her hair, as though the shimmering wisps were fingertips craving kisses. Then she said: "Ishtar, oh my beloved, has restored both our spirits to this life from another, so that we shall not be denied the joy of Love and the glory of Youth."

Ali closed his eyes, as though her melodious voice

had brought to him images of a dream. Invisible wings bore him to a strange chamber where, upon her death-bed, lay the corpse of a maiden whose beauty had been claimed by Death. He uttered a fearful cry, then opened his eyes and found the maiden sitting by his side, a smile upon her lips and her eyes bright with the rays of Life. Then his heart was refreshed, and the phantom of his vision withdrew and the past and its cares vanished. The lovers embraced and drank the wine of sweet kisses. They slumbered, wrapped in each other's arms, until the last remnant of the shadow was dispersed by the Eternal Power which had awakened them.